Mind

Traveling

Karma Banks

Foreword by Joyce Hennessy, MSW,

LCSW

I have tried to recreate events, locales and conversations from my memories of them as well as information gathered from complete foster care records from three jurisdictions spanning 15 years. In order to maintain their anonymity in some instances I have changed the names of individuals and I may have changed some identifying characteristics to protect the privacy of individuals. The reader should not consider this book anything other than a work of literature.

ISBN-13: 978-0996057707

ISBN-10: 0996057706

Book cover by El Issa Minkah

Dedication

This book is dedicated to my father John Thornton Banks who told me to always chase my dreams and that I could do anything, my aunt Katie Robinson who stepped in and made sure I knew who I was and where I came from; because of her I know the true meaning of family. This book is also dedicated to my grandmother Susie L. Robinson Burgess who showed me great strength and taught me the importance of spiritual well-being, a relationship with God, and perseverance. My cousin Joyce Coleman who believed in me, I give thanks for her although her days with us weren't long. This book is also dedicated to all youth having a past or present journey in the foster care system and to anyone who loves someone battling with mental illness. Last but not least I dedicate this book to anyone who has to mind travel to escape the

pain of the world we live in.

Love and light!

Acknowledgements

I give thanks to the Creator of all things big and small. I would like to thank all of my siblings for supporting me; we're living proof. I'd like to thank Lorna Banks, Joyce Hennessy, Gwen Dunston-Farthing, Sherry Bailey, Jerry Lorenzo Myers, Shani Pendergrass, Judith Wilson, Issa Minkah, Chawanna Gatling, Halima Johnson, Sandra Johnson, April Jenkins Hurley, LaShanda Hanna, Sydney Lamont King and many others unnamed.

Foreword

By Joyce Hennessey

Imagine gathering the shattered pieces of a past, untranslatable in its trauma, into a cardboard box. Inside the box, incomprehensible to a brain scarred by its own protective mechanisms, is deposited a life story unread. Karma Banks brought this story, and this box, filled with a chronology of court records, documents of a childhood in foster care, medical and psychological records, and case notes into my office. Her need to understand herself and her history was far greater than her fear of the emotional pain she might feel while reading and processing the numerous pages. Karma transcended the trauma of learning her history, as week after week, she arranged the pages of her past, reading aloud the self which society had constructed for her, then re-appropriating that self on her own terms and through her courageous creativity and writing. Through the innate ability to heal she cultivated in her youth, escaping sexual, physical, and emotional abuse through books, poems, writing, music, art and creativity, Karma established a foundation capable of supporting her future exploration of an identity whose traumatic beginnings she was determined to defy. Her memoir *Mind Traveling* details the power of the mind and its ability to facilitate healing. In rereading and rewriting the story of a life stolen by a broken family and a broken system, Karma, courageously faced and overcame an untenable life and identity. Her story details power reconstructing narratives of trauma into stories of survival, healing and inspiration for anyone who has ever suffered abuse. Karma's use of the written word as well as the spoken word in counseling provides proof and hope that is spite of the difficult beginnings, the mind possesses the creativity and power to rewrite and resurrect the self and she is surely a woman

recreated.

Prologue

Before my existence

I swam with persistence

Forgoing every twist and turn

Life was what my soul yearned

Initially I was a tiny wonder and

God sent angels to put me under

A tiny seed had been sewn

And into the world I was thrown.

November 4, 1975 was the date and most people were listening to the Ohio Players Sweet Sticky Thing, but in a hospital room at Riverside Hospital in Newport News, VA, lay Mama, a lone 20 year-old female, giving birth. I was so ready to see the world, but I wanted out a little earlier than expected…..six weeks to be exact.

Hurdling into the world, medical staff scuffled about looking for records of the pregnancy that were nonexistent. Mama had omitted doctor appointments altogether. She had been busy running, actually it had been her mind running and she just went along.

Entering the ring weighing all of 3 pounds and 15 ounces, I was ready to fight and that's exactly what I did. Even with a cardiac catheter and underdeveloped lungs I chose to hang on although I had no clue as to what I was fighting for. Mama had no clue and was going through her own troubles, but God's will allowed me to leave the hospital one month later.

From the hospital I was taken to live with my Grandparents and was introduced to everyone as Lavenia although my birth record notated something different. That was one of the games Mama played early on but no one thought to verify anything because everyone wanted to surround me with love.

Born into a big family everyone gave me love. First there was my grandfather. Teddy was a tall, slim very handsome man and was known to be quite the ladies' man. A complexion similar to that of a caramel Sugar Daddy candy stick; my grandfather had big pretty eyes that had a special sparkle, pretty wavy hair, big hands he used to handle the boys in the family and a big mouth he used to keep everyone in check. To his children he was not called Dad or Daddy, they called him Diddy.

My grandmother seemed to be the complete opposite of him. Grandma was short standing all of four feet and eleven inches, had dark brown smooth skin, slanted squinty eyes and thick coarse hair which she always hid under a wig or turban. Grandma was very soft-spoken and had two loves; God and her family. Grandma was a church going woman and was not into having friends. She felt that she had enough children to keep her busy. Eleven children were more than enough so Grandma never found the time or the need to wander from her bloodline.

To many my grandparents struggled but they called it making do with what you have. There had been a time when they had more, but my grandfather loved gambling and drinking. His habit cost him land and houses and our family was left to live in a housing project called Ridley Circle in Newport News, VA. During my first years at Ridley Circle and Dickerson Court, a neighboring public housing development proved to be my pride and joy. The projects were everything to me because there was nothing but happiness and family. Not knowing that we were poor, the projects was all I knew; it was my first love.

It seemed as if everyone in my family had a nickname and I wonder where they got them from. Along with the nicknames I'm soon to find that there are many secrets my family keeps tucked away.

Chapter 1

It's 1979 and here I am at three years old living with Mama, my little brother Fernando who was born a little over a year ago, and his father Winston. After seeing a lot, I have to remember a lot because Mama acts different. Not really knowing what different is, I know she doesn't act like anyone else I've ever been around. We live on a street that isn't really busy with traffic and we have a neighbor who Mama visits from time to time.

Mama likes to play games and I don't understand them because she never laughs but at my young age I've learned to just go along and play her games.

Knowing that it's Saturday morning because the cartoons are playing back to back on the TV in the living room I'm instructed by Mama to stay in my bedroom so I sit playing with my toys until Mama calls me, "Janera, come and eat."

Happy because I can smell the sausage biscuits Mama had brought back from Hardees I raced into the kitchen. Looking up at her as I wait for a greasy biscuit I'm surprised to see her face as she turns to me and says, "I'm not talking to you. I'm talking to the other Janera."

Puzzled because I know I heard her call me but her name is also Janera so maybe this is a game where she's talking to herself. Used to seeing and hearing her talk to herself, I go back into my room and resume my usual activities only to hear her screaming "Janeraaaa!"

I didn't know whether to stay put or go back into the kitchen since she had told me she was not talking to me. She made it clear she was talking to the other Janera. Mama runs into the room my brother and I share and starts to beat me and yells, "Didn't you hear me talking to you? You're hardheaded and stubborn just like your daddy!"

Going along with Mama's game, I cry as she beats me. Mama's different and that's probably why she cries all the time and sometimes I think she gets mad because I don't cry as much as she does. Something is different for sure but I just don't know what it is. Maybe I'm too young to know.

There are happy times living in Hopewell, VA and I enjoy going to the neighbor's house with Mama because that's where I watch Mork and Mindy. I love that show and I pretend that I'm in my own little space suit traveling with the duo because I get tired of Mama's games. While I chant nah-noo, nah-noo and try to make the funny hand gestures Mork and Mindy make, I can hear Mama talking, "Janera looks just like her father but I wish she would have been a boy. I didn't want a little girl. If she had been a boy, maybe her father would have stayed with me."

Not knowing what to think I continued to escape into the land of TV. Making the most of my time away from the house I play without Mama's unexpected beatings that came without warning. When Mama has someone to talk to, she doesn't pay much attention to me and that's a good thing. She would never understand the world I travel to. Mama is not allowed in my secret world.

My brother Fernando is a baby and he doesn't really do much but gurgle, spit, pull my hair and make noises and I love him because he is my only friend I have to talk to. Mama doesn't allow me to play with anyone and keeps us away from everyone except the neighbor.

Sleeping in the crib with my brother makes me upset because he pees on me. My efforts of trying to huddle to one end of the crib don't due to the lack of space I get wet anyway.

Being the bossy little big sister, most of the time I pretend that my brother is my baby and I take care of him because most of our time is spent together anyway. I guess

I act like I'm somebody's Mama anyway because my grandparents call me Lil' Mama.

Our mother took my brother and I on a trip to Newport News from Hopewell. In an unfamiliar place, my brother and I are left in an apartment. At first there were many people; all adults and then everyone left at the same time. Fernando and I are alone just as we are in Hopewell except we don't have the crib to confine us to one room.

Exploring the almost bare apartment I discover a treasure. There's a pot on the stove. Making my brother sit on the cold concrete floor I grab a chair. Doing as I had seen my grandmother, I pulled the metal chair and pushed it up to the stove. It's a feat trying to get up to the stove but I treat the chair and handle of the stove just as I do the railings of the crib and climb and pull until I can find out what the treasure is.

Pulling the pot I see there are beans. My brother and I are hungry so I guess this what we have to eat. Pulling the loaf of bread from the table, Fernando and I sit comfortably on the floor as I continue to watch the door and wait for Mama. She's taking too long and Fernando starts to cry. Looking at my brother he looks like he may be ready for a nap so together we go into the bedroom where we were left. There's nothing in the room but mattresses without sheets, no blankets, or anything but it's enough until Mama comes back to get us. Lying upon the bare mattresses as soon as Fernando is quiet I peer out the window and see night fall. That's a sign that it's time for us to go to bed.

We stayed in Newport News for a short period of time as the three of us bounced from place to place seeing strange faces come and go. Finally admitting that she needed help, my brother and I witnessed Mama's cry for help. Going to my grandparents' home we watched silently as Mama paced the floor. Always deep in thought she seems to never be able to make decisions. A strange woman introduced to us as a social worker is now questioning Mama and wants to know what the Department of Social Services can do to help.

"Look, I signed myself out of the psych ward and I have nowhere to go, no money and I'm tired of walking." said Mama.

I'm tired too but walking the streets is normal for us and it doesn't matter what time of day or night it is. If Mama wants to walk, we walk.

The worker asks Grandma if it was ok for us to stay with her.

"I would let them stay here but Janera already almost made me lose my roof over my head. I would let them stay but I can't.

"Well, given the circumstances, I feel that it's in the best interest of the children that they be removed from their mother's care. She is in no condition to care for them. She says she has nowhere to go, no job and no resources." The social worker picked up my brother and motioned for me to hold her hand. Together my brother and I are soon to be introduced to the foster care system. So the Newport News police officers assist Ms. Social worker in the removal of my brother and I from Grandma's house as she helped pack our things. Our mother was in no shape to do anything and is now sitting on the quilted couch crying hysterically. My brother and I look at one another and wonder why the police were called. Just wanting to be with my mother and brother, I begin to cry. Grandma rushes over to us and prays over us as she kisses us and slips two pieces of peppermint candy into my hand.

Overhearing that Mama has been admitted into Eastern State Mental Hospital, Fernando and I are transported to our first placement home. Nighttime has now fallen and the house looks spooky to me because it's dark. After getting a better glimpse, I see there's a tree with an enormous trunk in the front yard. With Ms. Social worker, we climb a lopsided stoop which leads to a big front door as I wonder if anyone is home.

Soon after Ms. Social Worker knocks, the door opens and there's immediate warmth. Feeling warm and cozy I see other children. Not wanting to talk I only stood and soaked in my surroundings as I clung to my brother. A stranger tried to pick him up and I shook my head.

An older girl ran upstairs and quickly and came back down and gives me a book. Not knowing how to read, I look at the pages and I feel no pain, no loss and my tears go away. Looking at the flip book, the older girl shows me how to flip through the pages as the characters seem to move. I see Fred Flintstone and chuckle in amazement. Getting lost in the book I allow the strangers to take my brother upstairs and clean him up because I've now been introduced to my second friend. My second friend is this book and I welcome it into my world.

Chapter 2

She tried her best

But her best was on a scale of its own.

She hid from a lot of pain, her mental state and

Sought the love she felt was never shown.

Mama ran and ran

She was running from her past and her mind.

She missed out on a lot of things;

Most importantly she missed out on time.

.

It's June of 1979 Fernando and I are back with Mama

and we're happy. After being in the system for almost two

months, I'm happy to see Mama and she acts as if she's happy to see me as well as Fernando. A bit surprised, we find that our new home is living with our Uncle Bo. He's Mama's youngest brother and he's short for a man but he's strong. Uncle Bo knows karate and watches Bruce Lee movies all the time. I love my uncle but I don't like his dog. I don't know what stinks worse, Uncle Bo's feet or his dog.

After being cramped into our uncle's one bedroom apartment for a week or two, we eventually make our way back to Hopewell, VA. Winston, my brother's father, isn't home much due to his hectic work schedule. At home Fernando and I keep one another company and even though my brother can't talk we have a secret code system that's mostly pointing and eye signals. He rarely reaches for Mama first because he's more attached to me and she doesn't pick him up much anyway. We watched her and listened as we are left by ourselves most of the time. Not knowing or understanding why we were separated from Mama for the short period of time, which seemed like an eternity, nonetheless, we're back together and that's all that matters.

Mama and my brother's dad argue a lot and today he's very angry and is accusing Mama of trying to take Fernando away from him. They start to fight and it begins to get scary for me. Never before seeing Mama fight anyone I continue to sit on the floor in awe as they yell back and forth until Winston grabs a Bible and throws it in the fireplace. Next goes in my mother's medication.

After that I see flames and block everything out as my mother grabs me and flees back to Newport News. My tears won't stop because for the first time my brother and I are not together. He's back in the house with the flames and I just want to be back there with him. Even with his peeing in the crib, I would be fine right now; I just want Fernando.

Continuing to cry and scream for my brother Mama takes me to one of her older sister's, my Aunt Mattie.

"Tee Tee, (that's Mama's nickname) where Fernando at? What's going on girl? You always involved in some mess. Why you just dropping the girl off," she asks my mother.

My mother is in one of her rages and when she's like that talking is the last thing she's going to do.

"Look Mattie, I told you I need you to keep Janera for a little bit. I don't have time to explain anything. Just take care of her until I can get back."

Just like that, Mama was gone before I could reach for a hug. People in my family don't agree with my mother's actions but instead they bite their tongues due to her fits and rages. Aunt Mattie takes care of me most of the day but after what I think is a walk up Jefferson Ave. I find that I'm being dropped off with my grandparents.

They're still living in the projects where there's always a lot to see, hear, and do. I get to see all of my family when I visit Grandma and Granddaddy. Uncle Bo always entertains me with his Bruce Lee moves and wooden nun chucks. As he flexes his muscles that's my cue to hold on to his arm really tight as he swings me back and forth.

Younger than Uncle Bo is Aunt Helen who usually goes out with my mother. Before their usual outing of dancing they'd be in the bathroom putting on makeup in the mirror. They'd be listening to music as they dance and sing. One of my favorite songs they'd sing is "We Are Family" by Sister Sledge. They showed me what they call a record and the picture of the ladies that look like Mama and Aunt

Helen when they're looking and smelling nice as they're about to head out the door.

My mother and her baby sister are so beautiful and many people compare them to doll babies because of their big bright eyes and cute pouty lips. My aunt Helen sometimes makes me dance with her in the hallway and I laugh the whole time because she sings and makes funny faces at me, but Mama never does. Mama chooses not to spend time with me, but that's nothing new and I think that's why my family loves me so much.

My mother stays gone quite a bit and my grandparents and the rest of the family are always left to care for me. Uncle Bo is my protector as well as entertainment. Granddaddy is gone a lot, but my grandmother is always home. Uncle Bo works as a sanitation worker for the city of Newport News and he's my hero because he takes good care of Grandma and me.

Most days as Grandma is watching her soap operas after fixing my lunch, I run to the kitchen window just in time to see Uncle Bo hop off that stinky truck. Running inside to get a drink of water we kept a secret. The strawberry milk Grandma makes for me and thinks I drink every day is handed off to Uncle Bo. As he chugs it down I smile and promise not to say anything to Grandma. He winks his eye at me and we slap a high five. Uncle Bo understands I hate milk but Grandma keeps telling me I gotta drink it for my bones.

My cousin Shannon also spends a lot of time at my grandparents' home because her mother works a lot. Pretending that my mother is at work too is what I do, but her shifts seem to extend for days and weeks at a time.

My older cousin Shannon is mean and doesn't smile much unless she's laughing at me. Even though she's mean, I love her so much. Wanting to hang around her she always says I'm too young. She always plays pranks on me and like a fool I always go along.

Grandma would always ask her to take me outside to play, "Big Mama, take Lil' Mama outside so she can get some fresh air." Taking me by my hand, my cousin hisses, "I'm gonna take you to get some fresh air alright." As I get onto the Big Wheel Shannon pushes me down a steep slope. Feeling as though my heart is about to explode I cry and run into the house. I'd cry and run and tell Grandma.

"Grandma, she bein' mean and she, and she," I couldn't finish what I started to say because my older cousin had cut me off.

"Shut up, you big tattle tale baby. You talk too much and that's why I don't want you with me," Shannon argued.

"Come here, Lavenia," my cousin calls as she chooses to call me by the name my mother told my family to refer to me as. "Close your eyes and open your mouth."

Moving closer I feel something isn't right. With my eyes shut and my mouth opened wide I waited and waited until I felt a big ball of something in my mouth.

Yuck! She's taken a big ball of hair out the ashtray and stuck it right in my mouth. I go running to Grandma.

"Shannon, let Lil' Mama alone," is all Grandma ever says.

Chapter 3

My Grandparents eventually moved out of the projects but they only moved up the street and around the corner. At first I thought it was far away until Grandma took me for a walk. The new residence is a tiny little house with a front porch, three bedrooms, one bathroom, a spacious kitchen and a back stoop instead of a porch.

Initially my grandparents shared a room, there's a room for my uncle Peanut, who has never moved out of the home, and a room for my aunt Brenda whom everyone calls Peachy. I think they call her that because her cheeks are fat and resemble fuzzy peaches. My Aunt is a little strange like Mama, except she doesn't cry like her; she giggles all the time.

Uncle Peanut looks evil and wears work pants but doesn't work in anyone's pie shop as Granddaddy says. He cuts grass from time to time and always smells like that liquor I hear the grown folks talking about. I think he's crazy so I stay out of his way because I never see him smile.

Other aunts and uncles drop in and out of the house to check on Grandma. I guess they know Granddaddy is fine because he's rarely at home anyway. He has a permanent seat down at the corner store with a few of the older men from the neighborhood. Every time I wander off from the house I sneak a peek around the corner and he'd be planted on a Marva Maid milk crate playing chess.

I guess since my grandparents moved out of the projects, Grandma has lost her fear of losing a roof over her head. Happiness engulfs me because I'm my grandparents pride and joy. Maybe it's because my mother is so out of it most of the time, they feel someone has to be there for me. Some of my cousins are a bit envious because of the time I spend with my grandparents.

There are many joys and I'm able to be a child as I explore my surroundings and not have to care for anyone else although I still long for my brother Fernando. I love to sit on the couch that's draped with sheets and lined with pillows my grandma makes by hand. I think Grandma likes all colors because I watch her make pillows of squares and cats and they're very bright. Some of the pillows match my pineapple, fruit punch and green apple Now & Later candy.

There's a coffee table that has two ashtrays and seashells everywhere. Grandma smokes Kool cigarettes and loves seashells. She paints designs on them with nail polish and other paint. She even taught me how to put them to my ear and listen to the ocean.

"Put it to your ear like this, Lil' Mama," Grandma said as she helped me place the larch conch shell to my ear with my tiny hand.

Looking up at the ceiling I start to hear the crashing of the waves hit the shore.

"I hear it Grandma, I hear the ocean."

That's what I love about her. Grandma never lies to me and she takes time with me. Even when I ask the craziest questions I can expect an answer from her even if she doesn't talk much to others. Grandma and I have a secret world filled with God's creations as she says.

"Grandma, I think I hear a bird. You know those birds I chase when we go fishing," I look to her for a response, which I know I'll get.

"Chile hish, (her way of saying hush) you know you don't hear no bird."

We break out in laughter as I want Grandma to go along with me but she just continues to laugh and swats my legs with her rolled up newspaper. The shells are one of my escapes and Grandma always says there's nothing wrong with feeding the imagination. She calls it creativity.

Sometimes as I listen to the ocean I take a pull of grandmas Kool cigarette casually lying in the big glass ashtray. Checking to make sure she isn't anywhere around, I'm clever enough to know if I hear her slippers coming from the kitchen, I need to flop on the couch and pretend I'd been there all along. Wanting to be just like Grandma, I like whatever she likes. She say's 'I'm too curious to be four' and claims that I've been here before. I don't know about that but I'm about to be five so maybe my five-year-old smarts are kicking in a little early.

As I put everything in my mouth, Grandma yells for me to stay out of the dirt but that's what I love about being outside. While walking home from the store on this beautiful day, as always I'm in my own world and lying next to the curb there's a beautiful marble. Grandma is in her own world too because she humming her favorite church songs and doesn't notice me bend down, grab the marble and dust it off.

Walking up the porch steps I put the marble into my mouth as I begin to sing and jump being quite the busy body. Gulp! The marble slides down my throat but not really. It's stuck and Grandma has already gone inside so I fling the flimsy screen door open and run to find her.

I'm gonna die, I think as I point to my mouth with one hand while the other clenches my throat. Grandma hit my back so hard the marble slid down my throat. Wanting the marble to play with I cried. Feeling as though I've really pinched Grandma's nerves I feared her sending me to bed. I hate naps just as much as I hate milk and my uncle Peanut.

"Chile, you can't go putting everything in your mouth. What's the matter wit' you? There are germs and you don't know where stuff been. Nothing goes in your mouth 'cept food, Lil' Mama."

Drying my tears with the backs of my hands I whimpered, "Yes, ma'am." Grandma should have known I hadn't quite learned my lesson.

Mama never visits me but sometimes she just "drops in" as Grandma says. On this particular drop-in session, I overhear Mama and Grandma talking about some pills Mama supposed to take to stop her from having more babies. An angry Mama surfaces from Grandmas bedroom. Running to her I try to ask her to stay.

"No, you can't go with me," is what Mama spat. "Stay right here with Mama. I'll be back. I promise." She storms out of the house. I know she only said that to keep me from running after her and crying. Usually I run to the flimsy screen door anyway and cry and tell her that I'm going to be good and wonder why she keeps leaving me.

No matter what I do or try to do I'm never able to make Mama stay.

Everyone else made a fuss over me when I had learned to tie my shoes at the age of three but Mama is never impressed with anything I do. I always tried to do things to make her happy and prove to her that I can be a good little girl. I'm gonna keep trying harder and maybe one day she'll scoop me up and tell me we're going to our own home to live happily ever after like they do in the stories Grandma reads to me.

With everything settled in the house I go to find the pills they were fussing about. The case is round and I don't think I've ever seen candy like this but since Grandma says I put everything in my mouth, why not. After trying to push a pill through the foil I succeed and eat one. It's crunchy and a little sweet. Wanting to see if the different colors have different tastes I find that they all taste the same. I eat a few more but leave some for Mama;

Having no idea that Grandma is monitoring the sweet

pills, I try to lie, but she knows better. Just as soon as

Granddaddy steps foot inside the house, she shares with

him what I had done. Granddaddy always tells her not to

fuss at me and she always does as she's told. Thinking

Granddaddy would get angry I'm now afraid because the

last thing I want to do is upset him with his tall self.

Everyone talks about how's he's as mean as a bull but to

me, Granddaddy is sweet as pie.

"Lil Mama, come on. It's time to take a nap."

Following the family's matriarch I pout because what I

hate more than milk is going to bed while it's still light

outside. Grandma tells me only lazy people sleep in the

daytime so I guess this is her way of punishing me. She

pulls back the crisp sheets and I climb onto the tall bed with

her assistance. Grandma must really be mad at me because

she didn't notice that I still have on my "clothes from

outdoors." I choose to keep quiet because I know I have really plucked some nerves.

As soon as the coast is clear and Grandma is back in the kitchen with Granddaddy and I hear them talking so I pop up and head over to her dresser. Her bottles of perfume are beautiful and they glisten along with the sunlight just like the colorful windows at church. Bottle after bottle, I experiment. Most of them smell like old church ladies. Growing sleeping from meddling or being a busy body as Grandma says, I fall asleep smelling sweet with a bellyache to match.

After waking I look around and see that I'm still in the bed with crisp sheets. As I yawn I notice the good smells coming from the spacious kitchen. Hoping off the bed I run to see where everyone is. My grandparents are in their favorite room of the house, the kitchen. Everyone talks, eats, cries, get their hair done, fuss, pray, wash clothes, and more.

The kitchen has a bright white porcelain sink with matching counter tops with deep grooves. There's a window over the sink donned with handmade curtains. Along the windowsill is where vegetables are placed to "get right." There's a gas stove, which is used to heat the house on occasion because they say there's no money to buy oil for the heater. Beside the stove is the back door and there are strings of cayenne peppers and garlic hanging over and beside the door.

My grandparents sleep separately due to my extended stay but come together to cook meals from time to time. No matter what we have they always make biscuits or cornbread. They both love to cook but everyone says Granddaddy is the better cook. I eat whatever he cooks except the catfish he cleans and skins on the back steps.

Granddaddy stands by the oven and yells, "Lil' Mama, come here. I want you to taste something with me." I rush to his side and get a big whiff of the biscuits sitting on the stove and begin to smile uncontrollably. He puts his big hand on the oven door and I wait as if I'm waiting for a prize. Pulling the door open he pulls out a long pan and peels back the aluminum foil. All I see are bristles so I scream and run into the living room.

"What you scare that chile like that for Teddy?" Grandma is angry but her husband pays her little attention.

Granddaddy chuckles and says, "What? I want the girl to eat some muskrat with me." Hearing the word rat made my tummy ache return as my stomach did flip-flops. Grandma tries to make me eat, but I can't even eat a biscuit. I wonder if this is her way of paying me back for eating the sweet pills.

Continuing to spend a great deal of time in the interesting kitchen I wonder who taught them how to cook. *Did they stay in the kitchen with their grandparents? Were they forced to be with them because their mama's didn't*

come home? They make me forget about her anyway

because all they give me is love.

Missing my Mama causes me to be mean to Grandma

due to my hurt and she says she understands. I think she

does in a way because she never raises her voice or hits

me. Most days I poke out my lip, fold my arms and sob,

"You aint my mama." As I storm out of the house, down

the sidewalk and towards the street Grandma always comes

after me and in one of her worn, cotton, button down house

coats with her usual bedroom slippers scrapping along the

front porch as she continues to yell, "Lil' Mama"

I hear her but I act like I don't. *I want someone to run*

after me. Oh, how I want someone to run after me.

Looking out the corner of my eye to see if she's running I

see that she's not. Those slippers probably keep her from

running because I know she would if she had some running

shoes. I'm gonna ask Santa to get some for her so she can slip into them when I play my little game I play.

Finally after seeing that Grandma is only up for standing at the bottom step of the porch, I give in and go back to the house. Still pouting, I ask, "When is my Mama coming back?" Not giving me an answer she begins to hum. My pouty face begins to loosen up and I realize I have no choice but to follow her as she goes into the house. As the screen door slams behind us we end up in the kitchen.

Usually she goes into one of the cabinets and pulls down a jelly jar or one of the millions of cups she gets out of the oatmeal canister and gives me some cold water from the spigot. I love the cups from the oatmeal canister. They also line the windowsill with pieces of plants grandma would pinch off to make new plants. When the sun rises, I see the sun beaming through the transparent cups with colors of blue, purple, clear and tan glaring down onto the white porcelain countertop. God's art is what Granma calls it. She says that we can find beauty in almost anything.

Still questioning where Mama is and when she's coming to get me Grandma just sits at the table and rubs her small, rough, dry hands and says, "Hish child." Hish is her word she replaces hush with. I know what she's trying to say and I also know that hish and hush means the same as shut up and go sit down somewhere.

Grandma starts humming then she turns to me and says, "Your Mama is at work, Lil' Mama."

"Where grandma? Where does my mama work? Is she gonna have a house for me?" That's what I wanted to hear.

Instead she says, "Yo Mama done got a job driving the Pepsi truck." Everyone knows that driving is one of Mama's many skills. They say that's how she and my father met. They both were driving cabs so her driving for Pepsi makes sense. Not knowing Grandma told me to just "hish", she had created a monster with that fib.

While outside playing in the dirt, which is one of my hobbies, Grandma sits on the porch sipping a pineapple Ne-Hi soda, which is her favorite. As we're "tendin" as my grandmother says, a Pepsi truck comes down the street. I take off running yelling, "Mamaaaaa." I run until there is s no more sidewalk and my short legs are weak. "*Mama didn't stop*, I think. I couldn't see up in the truck but I imagine Mama with all of her big hair blowing in the wind as she drives the big Pepsi truck. "*Maybe she didn't see me or maybe she'll come to Grandma's house for lunch like Uncle Bo does.*"

I cry and Grandma comforts me. She takes me in her short arms as she rocks me and hums. To soothe me she slips me one of the peppermints she keeps in the pocket of her housecoat. Whenever I see a Pepsi truck I look to see if Mama is driving.

From the front porch we go back into to the kitchen and Grandma prepares to do laundry. She rolls the washing machine from the corner and I sit at the table and stare in amazement. I watch and heard everything around me. She washes the clothes, puts them through the two rollers that wrings the water out the clothes, and then lays them in a metal wash pot which means they're ready to be hung on the clothes line.

There are a lot of clothes because she washes my clothes, her clothes, Granddaddy's clothes, Aunt Peachey's clothes, Uncle Peanut's clothes as well as Uncle Bo's clothes. Everyone expects Grandma to do a lot and she never complains. She just remains calm and hums all the time.

Wanting to help wring some clothes, Grandma always tells me it's dangerous. *Dangerous? Washing clothes? My Grandma must have a big imagination because I don't see washing clothes as dangerous.*

She fuels my imagination and I look at that washing machine as if the wide drum is a mouth and the whole machine is a monster. She said something about my arm might get caught in the rollers or something but her arms never get caught. I guess washing clothes is so much fun, she wants to keep it to herself.

Grandma does allow me to accompany her to the clothesline though. I'm too short to reach the line so I hand her the wet clothes from the metal washtub. I'd much rather be playing in the dirt by the garden anyway. There's a garden along the tall fence and she grows everything. I like the vegetables but what takes my breath away are the sunflowers. *"How can something so tall come from a seed so tiny?*

After the laundry is hung on the line Grandma somehow manages to get a big sunflower head down. She sits and plucks the seeds out. After she does that, she gets one of her pots out of the stove and boils the seeds in a saltwater mixture. Next, she sets the seeds aside to dry a bit and once they're dry she dumps them on a pan and roasts them in the gas oven. Once again we find ourselves on the front porch but this time with sunflower seeds.

I take a place on the cement steps and Grandma finds a comfortable spot sitting in the metal scallop backed rocker that squeaks lot. We also have Ne-Hi sodas and sip them as the cars go by. I say a silent prayer for the Pepsi truck to come back and I promise that I will run with all my might this time.

Chapter 4

My cousins visit my Grandparents whenever their parents come to check on their parents. I have a close connection with my cousin Man. That isn't his birth name but that's what we called him. He and I play and he doesn't care about my love for dirt because he shares with me a love for bugs. He taught me how to tie up June bugs by a string and watch them fly while holding on tightly to the string. As the sun sets we're still outside playing and that's when we catch lightening bugs.

My cousin showed me how to take the light out the bug and make rings and necklaces that glowed in the dark. Man is mysterious and I know he tells a lot of stories. That's what we're supposed to call a lie. We shared the same birth date except I'm a year older. That's probably why we're so close. We share the same special day.

All of my cousins liked visiting Grandma and sometimes they ask, "Where's Aunt Tee-Tee?" Whenever my cousins have questions about mama I pass down the Pepsi story and my make believe plans of her getting a big house.

They know I'm telling a story because everyone knows Mama won't dare stay in one place too long. I overheard Grandma's sister; my great aunt Margaret, saying that mama is like a gypsy and can't keep still.

How can mama drive a Pepsi truck and belly dance as a gypsy at the same time? My family is a bit strange.

Aunt Peachey is one of the strangest. She's round and always smells as if she's peed on herself. She drinks Sanka coffee all day every day, giggles a lot, and picks her nose. It's not uncommon for me to walk into a room only to find her giggling and talking. No one would be in the room. I leave out and go find Grandma.

"Grandma, does Aunt Peachey have imaginary friends," I ask.

Grandma tells me to "hish" and then she begins to hum. Never again will I question her about Aunt Peachy. My aunt has a son named Terrell but he stays away from me most of the time.

Granddaddy comes in the house fussing, "That boy ain't got no bidness sleeping in a bed with his mama. He too big fo' dat." I don't see anything wrong with it because I sleep in the bed with Grandma every night. My family keeps a lot of secrets and that's probably why Grandma hums a lot. Grandma says Granddaddy gets under her skin, but that's her husband.

That tall, loud man with the pretty wavy hair will be at that store all day and it's my job or my cousin Susie's, aka Big Mama, job to run to the corner store and tell Granddaddy to come home. I run and tell Granddaddy as I was instructed to and then would run back to the little house. The majority of the time whenever he surfaced from the milk crate he'd be drunk. Grandma helps him into the house and I sit on the couch and watch.

They walk through the dining area passing the big oil stove. Wanting to get a closer look I slip past them and hurry to sit at the kitchen table for a closer view. Uncle Peanut's room, which he now shares with Granddaddy because of my unannounced stay, is adjacent to the kitchen as is Aunt Peachey's room as well as the bathroom. Grandma makes sure he uses the bathroom before she escorts him to his bed.

Granddaddy slips and falls by the toilet and pees on himself. *He knows he too big to be peeing on himself,* I think. Watching as she closes the door I hear Grandma washing him up. My short Grandma surfaces from the bathroom pulling Granddaddy, as if she's been a quarterback her whole life. After she washes him and takes him to his room, I get a whiff of the Phisoderm soap he uses.

After making sure Granddaddy is tucked into bed she comes out of Granddaddy and Uncle Peanut's room, closes the door and begins to clean the bathroom. We don't have a lot but everything has to remain clean at all times.

Watching as she gets on her hands and knees to scrub every corner of the bathroom. She even scrubs areas that my Granddaddy never touched. We have a tub with feet. I call them dog feet and they scare me. Needing Grandma nearby whenever I go to use the bathroom, I imagine the tub running after me as I try to get off the commode. No one in my family has toilets, everyone else commodes.

After scrubbing the bathroom she gathers a stack of newspapers. Neatly she takes each page and lays them on the floor in layers. "Why you doing that?" I inquire.

. "Dis makes the floor dry fast, Lil' Mama." Grandma is so smart and I want to be just like her. She's smart, strong, she cooks and she reads all the time. Trying to look at the pages of the Good Book but that's all I did; look. All of the letters looked strange to me because I can't read yet.

Wanting Granddaddy to be responsible for us, after he sobers Grandma gives Granddaddy money to pay the electric bill. We waited and waited for his return but he didn't show up and after while the lights were out. Together we sit in the dark and still Grandma says nothing at all. Going into her room she returns with candles and lights them. Instead of having a big pot of beans, biscuits or cornbread Grandma and I eat tuna fish sandwiches by candlelight. Grandma doesn't fuss, get upset and she doesn't shed a tear. When Granddaddy comes through the door, she helps him to his room as usual and tucks him in. We finish our sandwiches and go to sit on the front porch. Grandma grabs her Kool cigarettes and her Ne-Hi soda.

Sometimes I think Grandma is too strong. Talking to the Lord and reading The Good Book must make her strong.

Today's my special day. I'm five and still have yet to go to school. Grandma baked me a chocolate cake early in the morning and that's all I care to talk about. I asked Granddaddy to get me some ice cream yesterday but he's been too busy down at the store.

"We're going to have a party," she said as she finished putting icing on the homemade cake. Her swirls were perfect and beautiful as always. The cake looks to have pin curls like Betty Boop's hair.

"Who's coming to my party? Are we gonna have party hats," I ask as I start to jump up and down in excitement. Grandma hums which means she has everything under control. I go outside to see what my cousins Shannon and

Terrell are up to. They're messing with the next-door

neighbor's dog as usual. He barks all the time and they're

always picking at him just as much.

They're over by the fence and I witness them sprinkle some

white powder stuff from some of Aunt Peachey's pills into

the dogs dish.

"Awwwww, I'm telling," is what I shriek.

"Shut up. Lavenia, you is a tattletale and that's why I

can't stand you. If you tell I'm gonna whip your butt,"

Shannon gritted between her teeth.

Grandma calls us in and the party begins. Grandma, my

cousins Shannon and Terrell and me of course are all that

was there. Today is my special party because I never had a

birthday party before. Not caring about gifts, being with

my family is enough. Shannon is sitting at the table and

cuts her eyes at me. I want to tell so badly but I don't want my butt tore up. She renders a sly grin over to Terrell and they both giggle. If Grandma catches wind of the "no good" the two of them are up to, they would get it.

My cousins and our Grandmother sang Happy Birthday to me. Not wanting to laugh much I waited for the right time for me to tell Grandma what they had done. After the birthday festivities we're sent back outside but something is wrong. The dog isn't barking, isn't walking and it isn't eating out of its dish. It's just lying on its side with the leash around its neck.

Looking at my evil cousins, I want to write Grandma a note to tell her what they had done but I can't write. Maybe I'll whisper it to the seashell and have the ocean relay the message to Grandma. Everyone thinks it's a mystery as to why the neighbor's dog died unexpectedly but actually it isn't a mystery at all. The dog has had an overdose of Aunt Peachey's nerve medication. I loved my cousin Shannon but I'm happier when her mother comes to pick her up.

As the months progress, the snow shows up and Grandma allows Terrell and I the freedom to run outside and play in the snow. We flop and laughed while hitting one another with snowballs. Terrell is taller than I so he's able to grab icicles from the side of the house. They are long, pointy and so cold, we eat them like candy. Our hands are kept warm with socks.

Since it's what Grandma calls the second snow she sat a pot on the porch almost directly under the icicles Terrell and I are enjoying. Once it's filled to her liking, she goes into the house and we follow. She mixes snow with canned milk, sugar, vanilla and a little salt. She calls it snow cream.

Terrell and I both get bowls of the sweet, snowy concoction as we make our places at the coffee table in the living room and dig in to our wintery treat. Grandma moves the big heavy ashtrays and seashells to make more room for us.

Soon, my time was up at my Grandparents house and Mama has come to get me just like I prayed that she would. She came with a baby boy and I'm wondering where she got him. Grandma always told me to be careful what I prayed for.

Chapter 5

Well, Mama came and got me and she tells me the baby she has with her is my brother. I still wonder where Fernando is but everyone acts as if he never existed. Grandma took me and had a long talk with me and told me that God will always be there if I ever need to talk and I can talk to him anytime. She also told me that I'm protected always. She told me to pray when I get up and before I go to bed and to keep stuff out of my mouth. Her requests shouldn't be hard to stick to.

Mama is with the guy whose father lives next door to Grandma. I knew I'd seen her go over there sometimes. She'd sneak by Grandma's house so I wouldn't see her. After a while I got used to it even though I still wanted her to rescue me.

All four of us go to a big house but it's not the big house I expected. There are quite a few people living in the two story house on Marshall Ave. We're still living in Newport News and I'm not quite sure how far I am from Grandma just yet.

Once inside the house we find that the upstairs bedroom facing the street is our room. I'm used to Mama's kind of living even though I don't like it. I find that the man who's with us is my brother's father. Not wanting to say much to him because he took my Mama away from me, I'm glad to see him say his goodbyes as Mama, my new brother and I get settled in the small room. Closing the door Mama brings me close to her. "Come here and listen to me. You are not to make a noise. If you do anything they're gonna come and take you away again. Don't ever go out that door." She pointed to the door that led to the common hallway.

My baby brother lay on the bed as Mama pulls me to another door. "This is your room right here. You are not to leave it unless I tell you to. Do you understand me?"

Not fully understanding, I nod as she opens the door which I now see is a closet. "Get in," she motioned. Doing as she says I step into my room and sit down as I look around. Clothes and coats hanging up are all I see. Mama closes the door, as I am to remain in my room.

This doesn't seem right. Just yesterday I was at Grandmas house with free range of nearly everything now here I am, back with Mama but in this little dark closet. Not wanting to sit, I kneel and notice there's a key hole. Squinting through the small hole is my escape. I see my brother and I see Mama rushing around the room. With my knees getting sore I gently pull down one of the coats to put under my body as a makeshift blanket. My boney knees don't hurt so bad now.

Day in and day out I'm not allowed to leave the closet unless I have to use the bathroom and even then I have to use the special knock to alert Mama. She shuffles me to the bathroom and waits outside the door for me. The bathroom here is nothing like Grandma's. It's not bright or clean and one day I saw a mouse hop out of the big trashcan. My baby brother Mitch and I are the only children living in this big house and I hope he hasn't seen the mice because it really did scare me.

Mama escorts me back into her room and then I go into my closet. I've learned to make it comfortable because I find that one coat is not enough so I pull another and feel something underneath my underweight body. Diving into the pocket I find a tube of Chap stick and take a taste. *It smells like cherry but doesn't have much of a taste.*

Not being able to see the window I glance at the hardwood floor through the keyhole to see if I can see the sun hit it. *Grandma told me to always look to the sun and there'd be better days and the sun is shinning all over the world.* I miss my Grandma and I wanna take back all the bad things I did but I can't. I'm stuck in this closet. I miss Granddaddy too.

As I continue to look out the keyhole, I see something new day by day. People come and go and if they sit on the bed I get a good look. My brother is always on the bed or sometimes Mama puts him on the floor to crawl but he can't really crawl. I want him to come to the door and get in the closet with me.

After taking a nap, which I do throughout the day because I can't play in the dirt or find anything to put in my mouth I see something different. Mama doesn't have on clothes and there's a man with her on the bed. My searching eyes try to find Mitch but I don't see him. All I see is Mama and the man and they're doing some moves like the wrestlers except they took off their clothes.

Being used to the closet I'm OK with it a little now. This is where I have to be until I have to pee or Mama lets me out. She's gone and she always tells me to NEVER leave the closet or someone will take me from her and she said she can't have that happen. Looking through the keyhole I see Mitch and he's hanging on to the bed by a blanket and he's about to hit the floor.

With my ear to the door I don't hear anything. There are no vibrations, which let me know that Mitch and I are alone. Mama told me not to move but I can't let my brother fall because if he does he's gonna cry loud and the people will get us.

Going against Mama's commands I run out of the closet and catch Mitch. This is my first time ever holding him and he's gurgling and smiling at me. I smile back and notice that he's smelly and his pamper is squishy. Not knowing how to change a pamper, I clean him up and do the best I can and he's so happy. Mitch is a happy baby.

Scanning the room I look for something to eat. There is cheese on the floor. Mama loves cheese and she cuts the ends of the blocks of cheddar and drops them on the floor. Sitting Mitch on the floor with me I gather a few small rectangles of cheddar and pick lint and hair off.

"God made dirt. Dirt don't hurt. Put it in your mouth and let it work," is what I chant as I hold up the cheese into the sunlight. Mitch is grabbing for it so I pinch a piece and feed it to him like I see my aunts feed the babies. He's happy and wants to lay down so I put him on the bed and fix the blanket.

Running between the bed and the window I make sure the coast is clear and Mama is not going to catch me out of my room. As soon as I see her coming down the sidewalk I slide back into the closet and pray that she doesn't find that

I've been disobedient.

Chapter 6

I hear that "the people" contacted Mama and want to know where I am so Mama has to enroll me in school. She took me to look for shoes with Mitch and his father. Mitch's father is a nice man and he talks to me. I see why Mama likes him because he's kind of funny.

"You're gonna be my little girl and I'm gonna buy you whatever shoes your heart desires," he said as he looked down at me while we walked through the store. Allowing him to see my smile I begin to skip and run to the shoes that catch my eye.

"Why you want these? Are these special shoes," he asked.

Nodding I say, "Yes, they look like Shirley Temple shoes and they might make me tap dance."

"Well, let me see you tap dance." Standing back with his arms crossed he watches me with a genuine grin.

Rending my rendition of what Shirley Temple does I make a lot of noise as I stomp my feet and swing my arms and round it off with a big Ta Daaaaa.

"Hurry up," Mama shushes us. "We don't have all day." Her frown is out of this world and you can tell she'd rather be doing something else. She never wants to do anything with me and I wonder if it's because I'm a bad girl. Mama likes everyone but me. It could be because I know her secrets but I won't tell anyone.

Finally able to attend school, I find that it's very different to be around other children my age. Mama makes sure she dresses me really nice; she washes me up with her AVON soap and lotions me up and greases my hair and face. She said if she dresses me nice and I smell good "the people" won't try to take me from her.

During story time I admire the faux topaz bracelet she gave me that's a little too big for my arm. She told me that topaz is for the month I'm born as she tried to teach me to spell my name but it's kinda hard to remember those letters. The last time I'd seen words was when I was with Grandma. Her Bible and newspapers had a lot of words but now Mama wants to act like I see words with her but I don't, not ever. Mama does a lot for those "people" and she says she don't like them.

At school I get to learn so much and I really like it. We make homemade butter and have a farmer talk to us. There's a tarantula spider to look at and an aquarium that we drop things in to see if they sink or float. Science is what my teacher calls the aquarium. After we have graham crackers and milk and line up to go to the restroom I drop paperclips and other things I find on the floor throughout the day.

My teacher is nice but mean. She does a lot with us but she is quick when she sees one of us doing something wrong. Her name is Mrs. Jamison and she has a little mustache that I look at when she talks to me. I wonder if she knows she has hair on her lip because I never seen a woman with that, only men.

During recess, I'm told that I need to play with other children but I would rather be to myself because I don't like things they like. Me, I'd rather experiment. That's what Mrs. Jamison says you do when you find out how something works. Grandma calls it being a busy body. Grownups are funny and I just like to do what I like. No one really talks to me so I make my own world and talk to God like Grandma told me.

We're supposed to be napping but I don't think anyone told Mrs. Jamison I don't like naps at all. Crawling off my blue vinyl mat I make refuge under one of the art tables.

One of my classmates sees me and she joins me. Not saying much we giggle.

"Shhhhhhhh," I motion for her to be quiet. "Mrs. Jamison thinks we're sleep. You want to see something," I ask her.

My classmate looks with anticipation in her eyes. Reaching my right hand upward from under the table I quickly grab a pair of scissors. Holding them up for my classmate to see I grab on to one of my ponytails and depart with it. Just as I snip I see Mrs. Jamison's big hairy legs from under the table. My newfound friend who happens to be my classmate scurries back to her mat and I just sit holding hair in amazement.

Mrs. Jamison scoops me up and my mind goes blank. This is my world, the only thing I know.

Chapter 7

The closet is still my room but I get to come out to go to school. I met a girl who lives down the street and she goes to the same school. Her name is Miranda and she lives with her mother and father. After school I go to her house and I don't actually notice anything except the fireplace. It reminds me of when we lived together with Fernando. Every time I go to her house I think of Fernando when I see the fireplace but I keep quiet.

Back at the house Mama is gone a lot and I learn that I can sneak out the closet and play with Mitch. We love our time together and now I sneak Mama's snack cakes one by one from the dresser. Maybe she doesn't notice or doesn't care but she never says anything. She doesn't say anything about the pampers I put on Mitch when his are squishy.

When Mama is home with us she cries a lot when she doesn't have company. Tonight she is out of control and screaming. I'm out of the closet with her and it's strange because I don't know what to do.

There's a man yelling and then the man is on the roof hollering Mama's name.

A loud crash erupts as glass spews everywhere. Mama shields my brother and I as I turn away.

"Woman, won't you let me see my son," he yells as he is getting cut by the shards of glass but still managing to find his way to the window.

"I got something for your ass. I'm in the closet so much I didn't notice that Mama's stomach is so big. I guess she hid it well but it's showing tonight.

Afraid for Mama, I start to panic as I hold my brother. Not knowing what to do, I freeze as Big Mitch, my brother's father makes his way through the window.

"It's alright, baby. I just want to see y'all I want us to be a family. That's all I want," he says as he grabs his arm that's cut.

Not noticing that Mama has run out of the room, she returns swinging a knife.

Mitch's father ducks and dodges as we watch with fear. He continues to try and find shelter from the woman who's pregnant with his second child.

"Police," is what's yelled from the doorway leading to the common hallway.

Mama drops the knife and begins to cry. She is not wearing shoes, which are her preference.

So much is going on and I go numb as my mind drifts and runs through my salty tears. I can feel that something bad is about to happen.

Coming back I see Mama sitting on the bed near us.

Trying to make Mitch "hish" as Grandma would do me, I

rock him and hum as his cries soften to a whimper.

Grandma told me I always gotta be strong because I'm my

Mama's daughter and she come from Grandma and we

strong.

The tall white man with the shiny badge talks and asks

Mama, "Can you care for the children? Are they safe

here?"

Shaking her head, Mama drops her head as she shakes

and cries uncontrollably. "No, I don't want to be a

mother."

In just an instant a call is made and we're gathered with

just the clothes on our backs and a few pampers; we're

gone into the night. Mitch's father is with the men in the

cars with the flashing lights and we're with a strange

woman just as Fernando and I had been taken. It's the

same situation but a different brother. Grandma should tell Mama that she's strong cause I don't think she knows. If I'm little and can keep her secrets and keep going I wonder why she can't. Grandma need to spend time with her so we can be a family and maybe Mama won't think someone is after her all the time and she won't leave us. Maybe but it's not today, not tonight. Tonight Mama is weak.

Chapter 8

This home has no children and there's a husband and a wife. They look like they're good people but everyone does at first. Grandma says everyone has demons, some more than others but these people must have little ones. It's warm here and feels good.

Now sitting on the nice couch I sit as Grandma told me to when I am a visitor in someone's home. Wanting to be good I don't say anything because I might let out a secret, maybe one of mine, maybe one of Mama's.

"We won't hurt you," says the woman. She's pretty, very pretty. She has beautiful skin and hazel eyes. Her husband is taller and he stands behind her.

"My name is Sunny and this is my husband Henry." The woman motions for me to get off the couch and take her by the hand and I do. Her hand is soft and warm just like her house. I see a fireplace and it brings back memories. I don't really like looking at fireplaces because it reminds me of the fire and the Bible and the medicine and I want Fernando.

Taking my eyes off the fireplace I allow Ms. Sunny to lead me down the hallway. The home is really nice and I've never lived anyplace like this. Good smells is what I smell but no food like Grandma's house. Clean is what I smell minus bleach and Pine Sol.

Looking up at her as we continue to walk I quietly ask, "You have kids?"

"No, baby. Jehovah never blessed us with any of our own but we love children."

Somehow I know she's telling the truth because I feel they're true blue as aunt Mattie says. That's when someone is about what they speak about. True to their word and she also told me there aren't many people like that in the world but I think most adults are good, I just can't talk to them because I got secrets.

"Well do you have any toys? Do you have any doll babies?"

"No, we don't have doll babies but I think I do have something else." Ms. Sunny went into a room as I stand in the hallway and she comes back with two teddy bears. "You think you might want to play with one of these," she says as she offers me one.

Accepting the plush toy I just look at it wishing it had clothes and hair. Led by Ms. Sunny, I soak in my new environment. After she shows me where my brother and I are to sleep she leads me into bathroom to cleanup alone. Looking around I see the usual toothbrushes, towels. They even have the butterflies on the wall I see in most homes.

Everyone mostly have the same butterflies but in different colors.

The bathroom is very clean and the smell of soap is very strong. Instead of the Phisoderm I see a beige soap. Safeguard and Phisoderm smell totally different and I can remember them with my eyes closed.

After talking to the nice couple and seeing that my brother is safe and nestled in for the night I'm led to my room. Not being able to fall asleep I listen to the stillness of the house and wonder how long we'll have to stay.

Days in this home isn't bad at all. Ms. Sunny takes us to the babysitter in the morning and I go to school while Mitch stays there during the day. I like school now but I don't like riding the bus especially in the afternoon. Something about the smell of the vinyl seats mixed with the bright sunshine make me sick to my stomach. By the time the bus drops me off at the babysitter I'm sleepy and my stomach hurts.

Back at the nice couple's home, Mr. and Mrs. Jones is what I discover their names are; everything runs smooth except for one thing. Monday through Friday the couple goes to work, I go to school and Mitch is with the babysitter but on Sunday instead of going to church we learn about the Kingdom Hall. That's where the problem is.

There is no problem going to the Hall, as they call it. The problem is what occurs before the Hall. My hair is the problem. I don't like to have my hair pressed and boy do I put on a show. I put on so much of a show Ms. Sunny wants me to leave the home.

Everything seemed to be perfect but I don't know how to be good while the heat is on my neck because it feels like I'm going to get burned. Yes, I'm scared but I'm scared of a lot of things just like that fireplace.

Thinking my brother and I will leave together I find that we aren't. When the social worker comes to the house only my belongings are sitting in the living room. Crying doesn't help so I look to the sun. Another brother I might not see again and people want me to be happy. Why can't I just be with my family? Riding off with the social worker, I watch the sun beam down as I forever remember the brick home where Mitch is.

Chapter 9

My next stop, or home as they say, is just sad because I don't have Mitch and I don't have Fernando. The house is a big white two-story home with black shutters. As soon as the engine of the car stops I turn and see an older woman standing in the doorway.

Walking up to a new place to live is the norm for me but I don't want it to be.

"Good day Ms. Harold. This is Janera." Turning to me, the woman with the briefcase says, "Janera, say hello to the nice lady."

As I continue to look down at the concrete front porch I manage to allow a hello to slip past my full lips.

This lady old and she don't seem to be as loving. Walking into the home confirmed that my new foster parent is old. The house is old and everything in the home is old. There are no bright colors like at Grandma's. It's kinda dark here, not much sunlight at all.

Days with the old lady are boring because we don't do much. She talks on the phone and cooks as I observe. I don't accompany her to her garden. Sitting at the table staring off into space hoping to be back with Mitch or Fernando is enough for me. We don't talk much but maybe she talks to me, I just don't care about what she talks about. She always talks about manners, being ladylike and what a little girl should and shouldn't do.

A little girl should be with her brothers but no one cares about that. All she cares about is talking on the phone, looking nice while going to church, her garden and cooking. The other night while I thought she was tendin' in the kitchen and I snuck to watch TV. Not being allowed to watch rated R movies, I commence to watch the Blue

Lagoon. Caught red-handed I'm scolded and sent upstairs to take a bath.

Bathing is not one of my favorite things to do so after I gather my nightclothes I go into the bathroom and run the water and just stand looking into the porcelain tub. Getting tired, I decide to sit on the side of the tub. Bringing my pretend bath to a halt, I splash the water a bit and wash my arms and face. Knowing that I hadn't washed properly Ms. Harold climbed the stairs and made her way into the bathroom.

Bending down to study the tub she ran her index finger against the porcelain. "This tub is dry as a bone. You aint wash, child," she shrieked.

"Yes, ma'am I did," spitting out my half-truth. The tub shouldn't be bone dry because it did have water in it, although not completely filled, but I had run the water.

This is the night I have to deal with one of my stories, my fib. Ms. Harold's mad is not like Mama's and isn't like Granma's I guess she get medium mad. She yells and points and then makes it her business to scrub me just like Grandma scrubs clothes by hand. To bed I go very clean and angry. Just like most nights I lay woke, drift to sleep a little and then wake back up thinking I'm in the closet but I'm not. I'm in a nice bed in a nice room but sleep is not nice to me.

Engulfing everything into my mind I think a lot because I never know what's going to happen next. I continue to explore. While sitting in the living room admiring a book I can't read I can hear the older lady at the front door.

"Come right on in. The TV that needs a fixin' is upstairs."

Peeking around the corner and down the long hallway I witness the old lady open the door for a man with a bag and he has on work clothes like Uncle Peanut wears.

Now in the foyer downstairs I look up at the long staircase. Ms. Harold is in the kitchen talking on the phone making some sour milk pudding. That stuff stinks and I hate it so I wanna see what's upstairs. Arriving at the top of the stairs I try to remain quiet as I make myself comfortable holding on to two railings and look into the bedrooms. The man Ms. Harold held the door opened for is in the master bedroom messing with a TV.

Unable to maintain my silent post, the man sees me and smiles. Not smiling back I keep watching. As he uses tool after tool, I'm amazed at what he's doing and he must know that I'm interested in his work because he motions for me to come over.

Lifting my small frame up from the stairs I do as I'm told and stand in the doorway of Ms. Harold's room.

Looking up from the TV the brown skin man with the mustache asks, "You want to help me"

"I don't know what you doin'," I say.

"I'll show you, don't worry. Come over here and sit on the other side of the TV."

Going to the front of the TV as he fiddles with the back, I sit Indian style as we do at story time in school.

"How you suppose you going to help me sitting like that," he asks. "Open your legs."

Doing as I am instructed by an adult I open my legs and watch as he continues to fix the TV and touch me in places that are not to be touched. My mind goes blank and I remain shocked and don't remember how I make it downstairs. The man never comes back but my mind is stuck there with him.

At night, not only do I stay awoke, when I do fall asleep bad things happen. Nightmares of people touching me and nightmares of my brother drowning in water, overtake me. Not being able to keep quiet while I slumber, I wake up yelling.

"No, no, no. Leave me alone. I want my brother," I yell. Ms. Harold runs from her bedroom and rushes to my side.

"What's the matter child? God, what's going on," she asks as she looks at the tears streaming down my face.

Telling her of the nightmare she gets me a glass of water and rubs my back. "I know just what you need," says Ms.

Harold. She exits my temporary room and returns carrying

a Bible. "Let's put this over your head. It should help with

the nightmares." The woman places the Bible above my

head on the shelved headboard. After we pray I feel a little

better and my mind and body allows me to drift off to

sleep.

My time is up here at Ms. Harold's, so once again I'm

escorted by government car. I guess this is what I have to

get used to.

Chapter 10

To my surprise, I'm taken to live with my Aunt Anne, one of Mama's older sisters. We're back in the projects with family and not only that; my brother and little sister are here. I feel like I'm in heaven. On my way over in the social services car the worker did tell me that I would now be living with my aunt. Honestly, I didn't know she had an interest in me like that but I'm glad someone in the family wants me.

Before Kora was born Mitch and I would go over to our Aunt Brenda's house and that's where bad things happened to me. Before the man who fixed the TV touched me, my cousin touched me. I used to love going over Aunt Brenda's because she can cook and my cousins, her children, are fun to play with especially her daughters Jewel and Laura. Jewel is the older sister and she and I both love, love, love Prince. Laura is more my age but she's younger.

When we would play school my cousin Brent, who's their oldest brother, would not allow me to go into the house to gather schoolbooks. He made me touch him and I can't take it out my mind. Sometimes I'm still stuck in the shed behind the house off of 79th St. not far from Newmarket Mall. I guess they forget I remember everything but maybe Brent didn't know because he always made me sit on his lap too even though his girlfriend lived next door. My mind just get stuck in a lot of things that happened but Grandma always told me I'm strong so I try to block things out and keep the secrets.

Right now I can't think about what happened at Aunt Brenda's cause this is a different place and there are no big boys. My sister Kora is a baby and this is the first time that I've seen her in a while so I'm happy. Mitch is his usual self, laughing and smiling, not giving a care. I wonder if he remembers what happened back at the house because I sure do. At my aunts place her daughter Shannon also resides in the home. Shannon's lucky because she's an only child and has to share her Mama's love with no one except us, for a little bit because I have a feeling we won't be here forever.

We're allowed to spend so much time together and I love it. Outside Shannon accompanies us and Mitch plays with his metal Tonka truck as I feel every bump in the sidewalk in my cast steel roller skates. I'm in a whole new world because I have to enjoy life. Skating down the concrete sidewalk I close my eyes and imagine I'm dancing to "You Should Be Dancing" by the Bee Gees and Tony Manero aka John Travolta is dancing up a storm. My short pigtails transform to Donna Summer hair until I fall and I'm no longer in the disco.

Not caring about a few scrapes and bruises because

they're nothing compared to Mama's blows. I'm just

happy to be with my brother and sister. Missing one of my

front teeth allows me to show a toothy grin as Mitch tries to

run over me with his big yellow truck. Kora is sitting on

the sidewalk just being a baby. I wonder where Mama is

just for a little but the music comes back on and I hear

"Little Red Corvette" by Prince so I gotta start skating

again. Yeah, my mind just works like that and music

jumps into my thoughts so that I can keep going. Grandma

says it's good to occupy my mind with good stuff and

music is the best thing I know other than my brothers and

sister.

This year is going to be the first time we celebrate

Christmas. Aunt Anne has been preparing for the holidays

and it's a change to see someone smiling every day. It's the night before Christmas and there are knocks at the door. I think Santa has to come down the chimney instead of through the door but we don't have chimneys in the projects.

We're about to make cookies for Santa but as Aunt Anne steps outside to greet the holiday eve visitor I hear a familiar voice. It's Mama, I know her voice from anywhere. I wonder why Aunt Anne won't let her in. They are sisters. I hear some fussing but I'm trying to keep my mind on the cookies as I watch Mitch and Kora play.

Aunt Anne rushes back into the house gasping, "I just can't believe that woman. She has three kids here and all she brings are some candles. My sister has really lost it. Kids can't eat or wear candles."

Looking on, I don't really care about candles but I did want to see Mama's face. Snapping out of my thought

Aunt Anne places the three red and green candles on an end
table.

"Come on Lavenia, Mitch and Kora. Let's get
everything together so we can make cookies for Santa so
y'all can get ready to go to bed. Santa can't come if y'all
up.

Mitch and I smile and Kora doesn't know what's going
on.

Somehow we burn Santa's cookies but we still put them
out with a glass of milk. Aunt Anne seems to like the
cookies more than Santa ever will so I think she should just
eat them all. Santa probably doesn't want to pick off the
burned edges. His gloves might get stained.

I'm the last to go to bed because I want to see Santa and
Rudolph. Creeping downstairs one last time I stare at the
cookies on the table. Santa might get mad and not leave

any presents because we burned the cookies. I'm gonna pray tonight and ask God to tell Santa we didn't mean to burn them.

Chapter 11

Christmas has come and gone at Aunt Anne's and everything seems to be great for the most part. We've move into a bigger apartment because there are so many of us. My cousin Terrell has now come to live with us because he was in foster care too, so I guess Aunt Anne is trying to do the right thing and help her sisters.

Terrell is a little like me because he likes to use his imagination as Grandma says. We're not allowed to go outside today so Terrell has a bright idea of making me a Pac-Man game.

"You mean you're gonna make one of the games from the game room? For real," I ask.

"Didn't I say I am? Stop asking me so many questions and just let me do what I have to do." Terrell is making clear that I'm getting on his nerves. Watching as he cuts the corrugated Frosted Flakes cereal box I wonder how is he going to put wires in the cardboard.

With the finished product in his hands I frown because his contraption looks like nothing I've ever seen at the game room. I want my Pac-Man to move and I want a joystick and the one or two player selection buttons. I know he don't think I'm going to play with that junk. My imagination isn't that big.

"What is this," I shriek with a frown.

"It's your Ms. Pac-Man game." Terrell places the subpar project on the dresser as I go to my favorite place to watch the neighborhood, the window of the room above the kitchen. From the window I watch everyone play outside and wish I were able to join.

Its summer and I'm glad we're on break cause I need a break. I'm a kid and I need a vacation like the grownups say. I'm fortunate that Grandma does come and pick me up on Sunday mornings to take me to church. Every Sunday I wear the same lavender dress but she says as long as it's clean, that's all that matters and she makes sure she cleans it for me every week. Grandma's preferred method of traveling is by pat and turner; that's what she calls walking.

Before we go into Zion Baptist Church we stop at the store across the street. Grandma always saves change for me. As usual I pick up Lemonheads, some Penny Candy and Johnny Appleseed's to suck on during service because everything is boring except the stained glass windows and the choir. Grandma always tries to get me to pay attention but after eating my candy and a few of her peppermints I get sleepy and lay my head on her lap.

Going into church I hold onto Grandma's hand, which is donned with her church gloves. I don't know why she gotta wear gloves to church because it's warm outside. She always says we have to be clean to go into the house of the Lord and we're always clean. From time to time, when the drummer goes crazy and people start shouting I wake to wipe slob from my mouth and check to see if service is over. Church takes so long and I go to spend time with Grandma and wear my lavender dress but Grandma always talking about a message. The message never gets to me but she breaks it down to me afterwards.

Walking back to Aunt Anne's apartment I ask Granma questions and if she knows she answers but if she doesn't know or doesn't want to answer she does her usual humming.

"Grandma, are you coming back to get me next week?"

"Lil' Mama, you know I'm gone pick you up, now run in the house and take off yo' dress so I can wash it for next week." Grandma brushes her hand against my cheek and looks at me. "You're a blessed little girl no matter what happens or what you've gone through. You are protected by God, you're special and I want you to always remember that."

"Grandma, I love you so much. You're my favoritest person in the whole wide world." I run into the end apartment of many located on 18th St., run upstairs, change clothes and rush back downstairs to give Grandma my favorite dress.

"Here you go, Grandma." I hand her the dress and she drapes it over her short arm and hands me a peppermint.

"I'll see you next Sunday Lil' Mama. I love you." Just like that Grandma kisses me and walks off. Amazed by her strength I just stand and watch her. My Grandma, the little short quiet woman who prays all the time and reads the Bible, no friends, a whole lot of sense and hands that can make nearly anything is powerful. With a bow legged walk I promise you my Grandma is meaner and can probably

beat Clint Eastwood. They say his walk is mean but
Grandma got him beat. She just don't have the guns and
holster. Grandma is armed with the love of God, healing
hands, kind, gentle words and prayer. My shero walks off
making her way to Jefferson Ave. She refuses rides all the
time so she can walk by herself. Grandma is unstoppable;
she is unbreakable. Neither Clint Eastwood nor the
Incredible Hulk can touch her. My Grandma is something
else.

Chapter 12

Its summer and I enjoy spending time with Terrell.

Exploring the neighborhood is what we do. From Ridley

Circle, Dickerson and Harbor Homes, we're everywhere

having fun laughing and playing. Mitch and Kora are

usually being occupied with one of our aunts.

Aunt Anne doesn't cook much because she works a lot,

so we go to Aunt Mattie's place over in Harbor Homes.

Aunt Mattie is always cooking because her boys play

football and they eat a lot. Their names are Kevin, Martin

and Lance and they play all kinds of sports. Aunt Mattie is

just like Grandma when it comes to taking care of the

home. She keeps everything clean, cooks, washes clothes,

irons and starches everything. She's even short just like

Grandma but they are different in a few ways. Aunt Mattie

will curse a dog out but Grandma never curses. Aunt

Mattie gets mad and will holler out the door while Grandma sends everyone for messages.

Family says that Aunt Mattie raised her boys, all three of them by herself and if you ask me, she did a swell job. They all have girlfriends; they never tried to touch me not even once. Brent is probably the only one in the family who do things like that. I bet if I tell Kevin, Martin or Lance they'd beat him up because they say they won't let anyone hurt me. I'm proud of my family even with all their secrets. They make me smile most of the time and there's always music.

When we don't go to Aunt Mattie's we run down to Zion Baptist and get a bag lunch. Sitting together, Terrell and I eat then run off to do a little more exploring but we always end up at the game room. The game room is actually a store that sells all the candy you'd ever want but there are arcade games lined against the wall and the teenagers challenge one another at Ms. Pac-Man, Donkey

Kong and Centipede. The only time one of us younger

ones gets a chance at playing is when the bigger ones aren't

around but as soon as they come back they claim

ownership.

When they're not bossing the arcade games I enjoy the

dance contests. The latest dance is the Smurf. Everyone

lines up to see who can do it best. Lately a guy named Pop

is the best. He probably practices on Saturdays while

watching Soul Train like I do. Most Saturdays I pretend to

dance like the Asian lady with the long hair as I put jeans

on my head and twirl while I do the snake. Not able to

make my young body move like hers I shake what my

Mama gave me even though Sharon says I have no rhythm.

Living "down the bottom" is what most refers to

downtown Newport News as. The most fun is had down

here. Sometimes my aunts walk us down to the store to get

snow cones. We walk past Maxine's, which has the best

cheeseburgers ever and then past the Moton theater. My

aunts always have something to talk about. I'm just happy to be with family.

For the first time since the beginning of summer we aren't able to get our free lunch at the church.

"What are we going to eat, Terrell?"

Pressing his nose close to the glass door Terrell takes a closer look. "Well, I guess they're closed today. We'll get something to eat. Come on let's keep walking."

Walking back up towards Jefferson Avenue I try to keep up with my cousin's long strides. I can tell he's thinking because he's walking too fast for me.

Crossing over Jefferson Ave. Terrell is not following the rule of always to hold my hand.

"Awwww, you're supposed to hold my hand. If Aunt Anne sees us she gonna get us, " I say as I try to run and catch up.

"Lavenia, shut up. I'm not thinking about holding hands because I'm hungry and I know you are too," is all he says.

Silently I continue to follow my cousin. We come to an abrupt stop in a parking lot and I begin to wonder why we'd stopped. We're supposed to be going to get something to eat.

"This is what we're gonna do. Lavenia, when I boost you up get in the dumpster and I want you to try and find something to eat."

"You want me climb in there." I say pointing to the gigantic trash receptacle. "You want me get in the dumpster for real or for play-play?"

"For real now stop asking questions." Terrell looks around.

I hold my breath and count to three as he lifts me and puts me in the dumpster. Not wanting to touch anything I close my eyes. *God this cannot be real. I'm in a dumpster and I don't know what to look for.* Opening my eyes I reach down and grab a jar of peanut butter and hand it to my cousin. Looking for acceptance in his eyes I see that my find is good enough. Terrell reaches for me and helps me climb out to stable ground.

Terrell opens the jar and scoops peanut butter out. "It's good," he says. "Don't you want some? I won't let you eat anything nasty and you see I ate some. Stop being a scaredy cat." Following my cousins lead I join him and eat the peanut butter, which tastes like…peanut butter. "Didn't I tell you I won't let nothing happen to you. You gotta trust me," he says. The rest of the day I follow Terrell trusting him while eating peanut butter.

Chapter 13

Something has happened at Aunt Anne's while I was at school and all I know is "the people" questioned me but I don't know. I don't know how my sister Kora got bite marks from head to toe. I was in school. All I know is she was wrapped in white bandages from head to toe and when Mama came to get us for a weekend visit she went off and hauled us to the hospital crying over Kora.

When we got to the hospital the doctors said that Kora could have died because of the severity of her wounds. My sister has been bitten pretty badly and while she was examined the nice nurses blew up the rubber gloves for Mitch and me. I heard someone say that Aunt Anne said Mitch bit Kora like that but I don't know. I kinda feel bad that I was in school because I usually watch over them when I can.

Whatever happened was really bad because Aunt Anne says she doesn't want us anymore. Something about her not being able to deal with Mama anymore, but that's what everyone says. Mama has a way of making people not like her. Granddaddy says it's her temper but I think it's more than that.

People always moving us for reasons they say are best but I'm confused and I think the adults are just as confused. It's hard to get used to any home because we never stay long. In the past two years I've lived with Mama, three foster homes and Aunt Anne.

My school is John Marshall and I like it because I hear that so many of my family members went there. School is okay but every day I wonder how things are going to be when I get home. When I am at school I'm checked a lot for bruises. This is life for me I guess. My teachers always know what's going on and I don't like it because I don't like people feeling sorry for me because Grandma said I'm gonna be okay no matter what anyone says or does to me. I'm just like the other kids; I just move a lot and my Mama got some problems.

Mama thought that we'd go back to her but somehow we're back in foster care. Kora and I are together and I hear that Mitch went back to the nice couple who kept us before. Why they want to split us up I don't know.

Kora and I are put with an old couple and from what I know; old people don't really let foster kids have a lot of fun. Maybe because they can't run so they don't want us to go far. The couple we live with now are the McCoy's. They are so old that the husband sit's in a recliner like Archie Bunker and reads the newspaper and watches the news all the time.

The couple loves Kora because she's a baby. They're okay with me but I don't really like them because they try to make me eat nasty stuff like TV dinners, brussel sprouts and fruit cake. My social worker should have wrote in my records that I don't like Christmas candy, fruit cake, brussel sprouts, black licorice, milk and mixed vegetables. They tell everything else but leave out the important stuff.

Old lady McCoy does babysitting and I think she just like to have babies around. I'm not a baby so I found a friend a few houses down. She's pretty cool and taught me how to ride a bike.

"You don't know how to ride a bike," my new friend asks.

"Nope. I never had one and never really wanted one because I have so much fun on my skates," I say.

After days of falling and scraping my knees I graduate to balancing myself on the pink banana seated bicycle.

"You wanna ride the motorcycle," my new friend asks.

"But all we have is a bike," I say looking around for a motorcycle.

New friend runs into the house and returns with a clothespin and grabs a magnolia leaf from the ground. She places the leaf and clothespin on a rear spoke of the bicycle.

"Get on now. We now have a motorcycle."

Riding tall and proud I zip down the sidewalk pretending I'm riding along with Ponch from the TV show Chip's. I'm one of the California Highway Patrol, badge missing, imaginary walkie-talkie, but I got my motorcycle and I'm coming around the curve of the highway. Just as I'm about to chase the bad guys, Mrs. McCoy interrupts the action.

"Janera, come on eat," she yells from the front porch.

Donning a frown I turn around to head back towards the house as my new friend awaits her bicycle/motorcycle.

"You coming out tomorrow," I ask friend.

"Yep, tomorrow and the day after that too," she gives a wide grin. Smiling back I run towards the house.

Inside the house I go wash my hands and go to the table to find the norm which is Salisbury steaks and gravy; attack of the infamous TV dinner once again.

Chapter 14

January 13, 1984, I'm now eight and I'm back with Mama on a trial basis. They say Mama has been going to her doctor appointments and it's been a little while since she'd been last admitted into the psychiatric ward. My new home is with Mama and her new husband in New Hope Towers on Ivy Ave. by the water. We live on the 8th floor and I really don't like the elevator especially when other people are on it. The elevator feels creepy but going to the 8th floor, I don't think there's any other way to get up there.

Mama is trying I see and she's talking to me which is different. She brought me a baby doll with soap and a washcloth and I make sure I clean my baby every day. Mama's husband's name is Mr. Billy. Billy Green is his name so now Mama's name is Janera Green. We no longer have the same name. The apartment only has one bedroom, which is for Mama and Mr. Billy. I sleep on the sofa bed, which Mama has made real cozy for me. Mr. Billy must be good for Mama. This is real nice.

We don't have to walk anymore because they have a 1979 Chevrolet Nova and it's blue. That's Mama's favorite color so I guess she may have picked it out. Mr. Billy looks like he'll do anything for her but then again most men will. Mama has a way with the men but she never wants any of them to stay.

Creepy things happen in the apartment building and it seems like people are dying a lot. Mama and Mr. Billy had a friend named Leon who lived on the 9th floor and someone did something to him and he's dead. I used to go down the hall to the ice cream man's apartment to get a chocolate cone or a pickle but he died too. One day, I even saw them take a body out the back door downstairs from the elevator.

Months go by and inside the apartment I keep myself busy by listening to music. Michael Jackson's Thriller album is my favorite. When the adults are gone I open the album and lay it on the floor and talk to Michael Jackson and the tiger cub. Pretending he's listening to me I tell him about my day every day.

"Michael, I had a good day in school," I tell the vinyl jacket. "I know you won't talk back, but I'm gonna tell you anyway. I learned about Martin Luther King Jr. a whole lot but I had to write a hundred sentences because I wouldn't be quiet. You want to watch Jacques Cousteau with me? You'll probably like him because he's always doing something underwater teaching us about life down there." Setting the album cover up on the carpet near the TV there's breaking news.

Flipping through the channels I stop to watch news about a familiar face.

"Singer Marvin Gaye was shot to death by his father the day before his 45th birthday," said the news reporter.

Eyes as big as my doll baby's I cup my mouth. "Oh no," I gasp. "Mama is not gonna like this at all. She listens to a lot of his music. You hear that, Michael?" Turning to the album cover I pretend Michael Jackson nods. The adults are jingling keys to come into the apartment so I hurry and close the album, place it back where it belongs and lay down on the carpet.

"What you doing, Janera," Mama asks with Mr. Billy not far behind.

"Nothing Mama. I'm just watching TV. Can you turn to Jacques Cousteau for me?"

Chapter 15

Mitch and Kora are still in foster homes and I hear
that Mama and Mr. Billy are making a better life for us.
They take me to school every day and Mr. Billy is smart.
He wears smart glasses and says smart words. I like him a
little bit I think. He seems to be a bit quiet for Mama. He's
nothing like Mama's friends; Mr. Billy is normal. A
regular Joe is what my aunt calls him.

Mama is keeping her appointments and I go with her
and Mr. Billy. The appointments are so boring. Having to
sit in the waiting area I find the place Mama goes doesn't
have anything for children. I'm used to reading Highlights
magazines and doing the puzzles but no puzzles while
Mama sees her doctor.

*Damn, Mama really played the part this time. Social
Services believed everything she said and she even married*

that nice man Mr. Billy. I know so many of Mama's

secrets and I know she don't like young men, she like 'em

old, at least that's what she say. I remember when she used

to take me with her to visit her old friends. I'd have to sit in

the living room or sometimes I'd stand at the door waiting

for whatever it is Mama did while visiting her "friend".

She'd always have money afterwards but she never tells me

what she does...behind closed doors. Mama should know I

ain't stupid and that's probably why she don't like me. I

know too much for a child my age, she says.

Mr. Billy is a nice man and he loves Mama. He loves us all

and this is so different for me. He does things for me and

he's the first man I'm not afraid to be around all the time.

Sometimes I think he's going to touch me like the rest of

them did but he never does. He talks to me and I'm not

afraid to look in his eyes. Actually I'm glad he's around

because he seems like he's smart and I'm wondering how

he met Mama. He's nothing like her other friends.

Miss Mary Mack, Mack, Mack

Make Mama come back, back, back

With a normal mind, mind, mind,

Please make her come back, back, back!

Eventually we move to Hampton. *The yard is small and to the left there's a crooked tree shading the small area known as the front yard. There's a concrete porch with no railing. Porches remind me of Grandma so I'm happy. I can jump off the porch without Grandma saying, "Lil' Mama, you gon' hurt yo'self chile".*

Racing into the house I'm excited and want to choose my room. I can't believe I'm back with Mama and I might have the chance to have a normal life or will I?

Can I be happy? I'm not going to be happy until Mitch and Kora come home to me. I want to live with them forever and ever... How can I live without my brother and sister? I can't go through the craziness alone. I pray that they're safe just like Grandma told me to do. She told me I need to pray for everyone good and bad but I surely pray for my brother and sister. I still pray for Fernando even though no one talks about him and acts as if he never existed but I remember. I remember all the things I wish I could forget but I'll never forget my brother.

Reality has hit me once again; I have exactly what I had prayed for.........to be back with Mama. There are plenty of children in the neighborhood so I didn't have to play alone anymore. My mind still spins, imagines things and replays past events.

Summer is nearing and school has come to an end and most of my days are spent hanging out with the girls across the street. There are four of them; two of them are sisters

but they they're all related. Tawanna is the cousin from

South Carolina and she visits her grandparents for the

summer. She's the one I really connect with because she's

closest to my age. She's taller than me; slim has perfect

dark skin with chink eyes similar to a black Geisha.

The local hangout spot is The Casbar on the corner.

Well, actually we don't hang out there. We just run down

there to get what we want and run back down the street.

Sometimes I'd try to swivel around on the tall barstools.

Mama told me I was to never go there because it's not a

place for children. Ignoring her, I went nearly every day.

We'd get banana taffy lollipops and dip them in Fun Dip or

Kool-Aid. There was a science to eyeing the perfect pickle

and we'd make sure we'd claim it and point it out as the

lady behind the counter fishes for the chosen one. During

the day the Casbar was a place to get treats and good food

but at night we all knew the adults were enjoying liquid

treats. While at home I can hear the laughter and music spilling out onto the street and sometimes I heard fights.

Nestling into life in the small house on Teach St. isn't too hard for us. Mitch and Kora are finally back and we three are so used to being broken apart and then brought back together. We're kinda like human Lego's, we crash and fall, but when we're back together we look perfect...on the outside.

Mr. Billy works every day and tells us he wants to provide a better life for us. I wonder what he means by better, this is as good as it gets. Mama never had us live in a house. We were accustomed to living in boarding houses with her. Mr. Billy can't possibly know what I've gone through in my life.

While Mr. Billy is at work Mama tries to stay home with us but there is something that stops her. When she runs out of shows to watch on TV, music to listen to, cigarettes to smoke or food to cook she goes back to the streets. I wish I can hire a private investigator to follow her. I'd hire Inspector Gadget. He'd need his Gadget Copter to keep up with Mama though because she's everywhere. Maybe I'll get Maxwell Smart. I wonder if he'll allow me to stand in for Agent 99.

Fearful that we might be taken away again she entrusts our Aunt Peachy as our babysitter. Aunt Peachy is not one of my favorites because she makes my brother fight me. Even though Mitch is younger than me he's something else. I was taught to never fight my siblings so most of the time I never fight back. My aunt also has a terrible stench due to her lack of bathing. Family members talk of how she doesn't have it all so why does Mama allow her to watch us? I hear most of the family wants Aunt Peachy to live with them because she gets a check so whoever she lives with will benefit because all they have to give her is $20, a carton of cigarettes and some coffee. I never knew anyone who loved coffee as much as Aunt Peachy.

Chapter 16

It's a bright sunny Saturday and I hear Mama in the
kitchen frying something. She's fixed corned beef patties
and a big pitcher of grape Kool-Aid and is getting ready for
one of her street escapades.

"I'll be back. Y'all mind Peachy and don't drink all the
Kool-Aid," Mama calls as she walks out the door.

Mitch and Kora are playing as I sit in the living room
watching TV. Aunt Peachey is on the couch giggling.

What's funny to her this time?

"Come 'ere, Lavenia," she barks.

She is one of the few family members still calling me by
that pretend name Mama made up. So in-tuned with Wham
on MTV singing "Everything She Wants". I don't want to
get up from the floor model television but I was taught to

respect my elders. Getting up I wonder if she's gonna make Mitch hit or bite me this time. She gets a kick out of that.

"Can you keep a secret," she asks.

"Yes, ma'am," I reply.

"You know you ain't the oldest," she tells me. My aunt has definitely lost it. Everyone knows I'm the oldest. There's me, my brother Fernando, Mitch and Kora.

"What do you mean?" I ask with a confused look because I didn't know what she would say next.

I don't know what it is but something tells me that Aunt Peachey isn't as crazy as everyone is making her out to be. She has more sense than everyone gives her credit for and I have a feeling that what she's about to tell me will change my life forever.

Watching her part her tobacco smoked lips, she spits out words like they're a big wad of day old gum, that lost its flavor.

"You know your Mama had a baby before you. She white and her name is Rachel."

I don't know what to say but at this moment I have resentment for my aunt. I feel as though she's out to hurt me. Why would she tell me something like that? I take pride in being the oldest. Little Janera is what they call me. I was named after my mother so it is me who's supposed to be like Mama and take care of Mitch and Kora.

In a daze I stumble to my room confused and stay there for the remainder of the day. Even if Aunt Peachy is telling the truth, what happened to adults protecting me? Why won't anyone protect me?

When I think I can get out of my head and live life there is something else to face. There is no way I can tell my Mama. She'll try to kill me and Aunt Peachy both. Secrets...what's up with the family secrets?

The end of the summer brings the end of my friendship with Tawanna and the trips to the Casbar. I have to resort to playing with my siblings once again which isn't all that bad...they just don't understand big sister stuff and Tawanna does because she also has a little brother.

Chapter 17

Life on Teach Street settles me and my siblings into some normalcy. When the school year begins Mitch and I go to school while Kora is left home with Mama. I often wonder what they're doing while I'm in school and when I get home I make sure my sister is okay. On weekends Mr. Billy works just as he does during the week and Aunt Peachy comes over to babysit us.

Weekends mean Mama wants to break free so she can hang with Ms. Nicky or Ms. Rosa. Ms. Nicky lives directly across the street from us and is Tawanna's aunt. The Fords who live next to Ms. Nicky are her parents. Ms. Rosa lives down the street and stays drunk all the time. Her husband tries to get her to stay home just as Mr. Billy does with Mama. Ms. Nicky isn't married but she has three daughters. I play with two of them but one of them never leaves the house and can't talk. At night while Mama and

Ms. Nicky are out, I watch Ms. Nicky's house from the living room window. I worry about her daughter because she doesn't have an older sister like myself to watch out for her. Hearing she is the big sister makes me sad.

Keeping up with fashions and fads are important to Mama and she loves to look good. She has gotten out of her Chaka Khan phase and is entering Tina Turner mode. One day she came home with a spiked wig and a tight leather miniskirt. Mr. Billy pleaded with her to stay home and spend time with us.

"Why you wanna keep me couped up in the house Billy?" she yells.

Mr. Billy just shakes his head and paces the floor.

"You don't spend any time with your kids and you're spending too much money. I work for the household not for entertainment purposes."

One day Mama and Ms. Nicky went grocery shopping and it seems they have other important errands to run because they both drop groceries off and leave again. Mr. Billy and I are left to put groceries in cabinets, the refrigerator and freezer but no one's at Ms. Nicky's to put away groceries because I later hear that TamTam, the oldest daughter ate raw eggs and ground beef. I often wonder what would make mothers want to stay away from their children. I begin to think Mama hates being home or maybe she just hates us.

Chapter 18

Leaving the house on Teach Street I hear that our step daddy Billy purchased a home for us. Being that we never lived in a home let alone a new house and I figure Mr. Billy really loves Mama he might even love us.

Life seems to be just fine. Kora and I share a bedroom next to our parents and Mitch has his own room. There's a huge eat in kitchen with a window over the sink just like Grandmas house and there's a laundry room off to the right. Walking to the laundry room, which is adjacent to the kitchen, is the back door; it is actually off to the side of the house. Both front and back porch smell of fresh lumber. The living room is simple and our mother has requested that all furniture be blue because it's her favorite color. Everything is to be kept neat and clean just the way she wants. She seems to have every reason to stay home now. We're far away from Ms. Nicky and don't have to worry about Mama running off but I have a feeling that things are going to take a turn for the worse.

Going to school renders normalcy for my brother Mitch and I. We go to school every day but there's one problem; my brother has a mouth on him, meaning he talks too much especially when it comes to the older kids at the bus stop. Not wanting any problems I keep quiet and advise my brother to do the same. He can't stand and wait for the bus like a regular kid because running that mouth is his favorite pastime and it always results in an argument. Watching some of the other kids stand and play with silence I wish Mitch would find silence too but he never does. I'm glad to see our cheese bus approaching.

Putting the morning bus stop situation behind me I wonder why Mitch didn't ride the bus home with me.

Mama probably picked him up early. She's always treating him special but I'm used to it now; he has lighter skin and is a boy. If you're one of the two you're at an advantage with Mama.

Eleven years of my life and it seems like Mama is always gonna be the same. Walking up the sidewalk I smell spaghetti cooking which is an indicator that Mama is in a good mood; good mind. For as crazy as she gets at times, she loves to cook and that means no crying and screaming. Everyone says she gets her cooking skills after Granddaddy who can burn like nobody's business.

Mama always makes garlic bread with spaghetti and I also smell it. I absolutely love garlic bread especially when the outside is crusty so I can't wait to eat. Since Mama is in a good mood I'll try to tell her about my day. Using the back/side door as Mama instructs us to do I tiptoe because I wanted to surprise Mama with my good news about my progress report. Besides, she said she doesn't want us tracking dirt on the carpet in the living room so using the front door is not an option.

Turning the doorknob I prepare to tell Mama how my day went in school, I try to win her with my bright smile everyone else loves. As soon as I take three steps through the door my huge smile turns to fear. BAM!!!!! Mama's fist meets my face and I go down to the floor without anyone counting to three. I'm met by stars before my eyes and begin to feel woozy. Trying to figure what is going on I try to listen to her rants or clues this time.

"You let them boys at the bus stop beat up on your brother. I'm gonna show you," she yells.

Finding that it's hard trying to pick myself up from the floor I cry. Afraid and angry now because I know Mitch and his big mouth are behind this storm inside of Mama. Her emotions are like a storm to me because you never know what you're gonna get; very much described as unpredictable. One day it might be sunny and then midway through, there's a thunderstorm.

"Mama, no! I'm gonna be good. He's not telling the truth. I wouldn't let anyone beat up Mitch. He keeps running his mouth to the older boys at the bus stop." Wishing for an escape I start to think fast but Mama is faster today.

Watching as she runs to the hall closet I clutch my friend silence. Silence surrounds me all the time anyway and hugs me because we are forbidden from speaking unless told to do so. Mama returns, clutching a hammer with both hands, raising it over her head like she's about to serve a volleyball.

"Nooooo!" I scream. "Mama, please no!"

I can't do anything to stop her and my cries go unanswered so I drop to my knees and slide onto the linoleum floor. Crawling on my knees I attempt to hide underneath the glass table which seats six. Knowing her love for her furniture I don't think she'd want to do anything to the glass table Mr. Billy paid for with his hard earned money but something seems terribly wrong this time. The storm is getting worse and there's now a tsunami in the kitchen. I'm guessing Mama hasn't been taking her medication.

CRASH! Mama tossed the iron atop the table. Thinking I've found refuge I remain in a huddled position under the glass table as all the glass shatters on me. My bottom is glued to the linoleum and I clutch my knees to my chest as I tuck my head downward to prevent glass from hitting my face. All I can do is close my eyes and pray to God.

"Dear God, I'm scared help me. Help Mama..." Before I can gather my thoughts and finish my prayer I'm being pulled.

A portion of the glass table remains standing but there is glass everywhere. Looking into Mama's face, I avoid her eyes but try to see if she is back to normal...her normal, but she isn't. Grabbing me by the collar of my shirt she yanks me up and everything starts to move in slow motion. A sharp pain to my right arm interrupts my mind traveling. As Mama pulls me, my arm is sliced by the part of the table still standing. I'm too scared to hurt. Too afraid to feel the pain, I just go numb seeing the blood and I'm a rag doll. I'm limp and Mama can do what she wants. My short years on earth have been hell so I'm prepared for what's next.

This is the end. I know it. She's going to kill me today, as I'm still the ragdoll. My body is limp but my mind continues to travel. The record is still spinning as the needle is lifted as Neil Diamond sings Sweet Caroline. Closing my eyes my mind goes limp along with my body and Mama shrieks.

"Damn it!" As she's pulling me, the glass slices her arm as well but on the left. Now there's more blood. Coming back to life my body slowly begins to come back to move. Both of us, mother and daughter have white flesh showing as if we've just received matching tattoos but I'm still too afraid to speak or cry loudly.

"Get your ass up. Look what you made me do," she snaps.

Still in a daze of confusion I slowly begin to get up as glass falls from my body. My mind has now traveled back fully to the food on the stove but now we don't have a table. She probably wasn't going to let us eat anyway. Meals are a privilege at home not a necessity.

Mama pulls me despite her wound, which is worse than mine. Back into the dungeon I go. My jail cell actually.

"Stay there and don't you come out."

Not knowing why she always tells me not to come out because there's a padlock on the other side of the door. I can't get out if I tried to. Reality hits me and I cry harder and louder as the pain sets in. I'm bleeding badly and so is Mama. Hoping she'll drive us both to the hospital because I know the cuts is serious, but knowing exactly who my Mama is, that thought is quickly erased. Having to think quickly I go to the closet and get a shirt to wrap my wound applying pressure. Watching the A-Team and McGyver at Grandmas house sure comes in handy.

Grabbing a cotton belt used for a dress I use my teeth to wrap my makeshift bandage around my arm making sure not to tie it too tight. Remembering not to make it too tight I make sure I can wedge two fingers between the bandage and my arm. I read about tourniquets and they're only used in times of extreme desperation.

Now that I've doctored myself I realize that I didn't die. I'm here, protected like Grandma said. Boy, she'd be mad if she knew Mama is acting like this and Granddaddy would probably go upside her head. He said no one is to hurt me ever and he stopped her from doing bad things to me as a baby. Granddaddy said I've been through enough as a child and that Mama should leave me alone and let me be a child.

Mama probably has no thought of taking me to the hospital but she has return to my room to toss in a metal pail because she knows that Kora and I are going to need to use the bathroom. Instead of the pail she tosses in my little sister. I'd rather know that Kora's on the inside with me rather than the other side with mean Mama. I can tell that she hasn't had her medication.

Days and nights are really long now because Mama is to
the point where she doesn't want to see us at all so not only
do we have to stay in our rooms but she has put padlocks
on the doors 24/7. There's one good thing about the
padlocks though. The locks give us the ability to know
when she's in a mood to beat us or yank us around.
Without the padlocks Mama just bursts into the room or
sometimes hides behind the door and jumps out.

She can't jump out unannounced because the warning of
the jingle of keys, clicking and clanking, then the insertion
of the keys into the lock, the yanking of the padlock and
then the turn of the doorknob and she's in. The sequence
of warning signals gave Kora and I enough time to jump
into our beds and pretend to be sleep.

As big sister it's my job to watch over my siblings, but I
know Mitch's treatment isn't as bad because she treats him

different. With Kora as my roommate it's also my duty to keep her entertained by reading to her. She doesn't want to get out of bed most of the time so I read my Judy Blume books to her as she looks at the ceiling. Kora hangs on the best way she can and I'm always here for her.

Remembering that Grandma always told me lazy people lay in the bed all day I resort to the carpeted floor, which I find to be quite comfortable. The only time I hop into bed when it's bedtime or when we hear the warning signals that Mama is about to enter our room.

Only being allowed to go to school that's where we eat our meals because the privilege of eating at home has been stripped. Eating is not a necessity Mama says and there are now chains and a padlock barring us from the refrigerator.

Get up in the morning and get ready for school I pray and ask God to watch over everyone good and bad because that's what Grandma says I should do. We only bathe when we're allowed to.

Kora is still in bed when I leave for school but that's where she spends most of her time anyway. My sister seems sad all the time and I try to cheer her up with my stories.

She had already removed the lock so leaving my bedroom I know to walk down the short hallway into the kitchen and out the back door like clockwork. Mama listens for steps and counts them. Some of the people have said Mama thinks we'll kill her. That's her mind. People have been after Mama for years.

Today I notice the chain and padlock are not draping the refrigerator so quietly I open the freezer and my eyes scan the food. Quickly I grab a frozen corndog and stuff it into my book bag. Next I sling my book bag over my shoulder and make my exit and head to the bus stop. I make sure to step loud because she's counting.

Knowing that the hotdogs on a stick will thaw during the school day I learn how to get them without Mama knowing. I make frequent trips to the coat closet at school and take bites of the corndog and put it back in my book bag.

At school my teacher begins to wonder why I keep going into the coat closet. Never minding what she thinks I continue to make my frequent breaks from the class to devour more of the thawing corndog. Cramming the corndog back into my backpack I look to my left and there is Mrs. Aster. My full mouth prevents me from saying anything but silently I beg her to keep my secret of hunger. Her eyes drop as she instructs me to get back to my seat promising to keep hush with solemn eyes.

Chapter 19

Life on Lincoln Street is getting creepier and creepier. From being padlocked in our bedrooms to watching Mama cooks food for the dogs and not us; it just doesn't make sense to me. People come by the house to check on us but Mama tells them lies about us visiting our stepfather's family. Mr. Billy's family doesn't like Mama at all so why would they keep us? They try to feed us when we visit but Mama always gives us strict instructions to say that we've just eaten when we really are hungry.

When we do eat it's because Mr. Billy attempts to feed us. It's funny to me because it's my job to check my brother and sister's food and if it's not done I take it back to the stove as Mr. Billy and I stand and watch the chicken as if it's a main attraction. To me it is a main attraction because it's a special occasion whenever we have food.

Mama's husband comes to my rescue sometimes and even argues with Mama over the way she treats us but he never wins. Our stepfather tries to spend quality time with me whenever Mama allows him to. Finding that I love science he introduced me to my first microscope. With the microscope my mind travels to a scientific world I keep secret. Analyzing spores and making slides with bugs, fibers and anything else I find interesting is fun. Deep down I don't believe Mama likes the bond Mr. Billy and I have formed. He has a genuine interest in my siblings and me but Mama only wants Mr. Billy to play in her world.

After what seems to be a good day for Mama she goes into one of her rages once again.

She yells, "She can't stay her black ass in here. I'm not going to have her in my house anymore."

Bewildered by what I could have possibly done Mama grabs me. Talking or asking questions is not an option anymore that's why I gotta mind travel and stay in my head thinking, planning and reading; talking only makes her angrier. After dragging me through the kitchen she shoves me out onto the back porch.

"Sleep your ass out there with the dogs."

There's no need to wonder why Mama hates me so much because I know she has issues. As I'm mind traveling, Mr. Billy comes to the door, tells me how he doesn't like what she does and shakes his head. Mama was fussing and hitting him before she stormed away. She ran away from this beautiful home, away from us, away from Mr. Billy who loves her very much.

Wanting any excuse to try and go into the house I knock on the door.

"I gotta use the bathroom," I whisper as Mr. Billy opens

the door. Mr. Billy helps me sneak into the house and

although Mama is nowhere near the home, we're both

afraid of what might happen if she were to return and find

me inside instead of on the back porch with the dogs. After

using the bathroom, on my way outside my stepfather

hands me a blanket. With my eyes I render a silent thank

you.

I wonder why he never stands up for himself and allows

Mama to push him around. I loved him so much but I wish

he'd grow a backbone. I'll never marry a pushover like my

stepfather.

Back to the porch I go and nestle myself on the wooden

porch with my blanket. King and Tracy our beautiful

German Shepherds come to my aid and nestle with me.

King is black and looks like a police K-9 and Tracy is a

dull white. I talk to our dogs all the time and they protect me. My canine friends hold my secrets, listen as I cry and never allow anyone near me. They care for me more than Mama. Tears are flowing as I continue to replay the events of today and wonder what I've done. Snuggling closer to the dogs I dry my tears until I can no longer fight sleep.

Mama has good and bad days and I can tell most of the time the type of day she's going to have. Today must be a good day because she told me she wants to talk to me.

"Your Daddy wants to see you. He's in town"

Looking at her I look into her face and can tell this indeed is a good day. Her lips are relaxed and not twisted or scrunched. Not knowing what to say I just nod and escape back into my thoughts; proceed to mind travel staring at the Bootsy Collins and Air Supply album covers.

She told me he never wanted to be with her and that he

didn't want me either. What makes him want to see me

now? I remember my aunts telling me he loves me but

dislikes Mama's ways. Will he like me? Is what Mama said

about him true, I think as I sit on the sofa we're barely

allowed to sit on when we're not locked in our bedrooms.

Preparing for my father's visit, I begin to dream of him

sweeping me away and never having to deal with her

craziness again.

Daddy's gonna whisk me away from here and I'm gonna

leave this dungeon. I'm gonna have a life of smiles and I

hope I won't have to cry as much with him. I'm gonna

leave those days of being in foster care behind. Nobody will

probably touch me with Daddy. He'll watch over me.

As I travel back to reality I realize there's one thing that

makes me hold on to Mama; my siblings. Leaving Mitch

and Kora to reside with her by themselves is gonna kill me

literally because I can't imagine her hurting them. She'd probably kill them for sure.

If I'm her target now, who's going to be her target when and if I leave? My love for my siblings runs deep but I know Mama is sick and needs help. She'll kill Kora for sure because she's the smallest and she doesn't know how to think fast like me. My little sister waits for my cues. We have a system down that only she and I understand. My eyes tell her that I'll take the beating or sometimes I'll purposely do something to draw attention off Kora. Being big sister means I can take more than my younger siblings and no one knows all the stuff I've been through already. Grandma said I'm strong and although I'm stronger I'm no match for Mama. It'll only be a matter of time before one of us dies.

Chapter 20

Oh happy day....

Oh happy day....

When Daddy comes....

Falalalalaaaaaa

Mama is getting me ready for my Daddy's arrival. She pulled the new clothes out of the closet that she keeps just in case a social worker visits. Dressed nicely with my tight ponytails and face greased, I'm allowed to sit on the sofa which is usually off limits. Sitting with silence I keep my hands folded and placed on my lap pretending to be the perfect child Mama wishes for. Mitch and Kora are seated on the floor in front of the television. With everyone out of the room today is definitely good. For some strange reason ever since Mama told me about my Daddy visiting she's calmed down quite a bit.

My heart is racing and I begin to think, *Will Daddy have anything to say to me? Why does he want to meet me now? Is Mama going to let me go live with him?*

Snapping out of my thoughts I make sure my ponytails are still laid down on the side with the Blue Magic hair grease Mama used. I'm just glad she didn't use that Dax stuff that smells bad.

There are knocks at the front door but I know to stay seated until Mama tells me otherwise. Feeling like I'm on the Price is Right and Bob Barker is about to show me what's behind Door #1 I feel as if my heart is going to jump out my chest. The palms of my hands are really sweaty and have begun to drip. I wipe them on the blue couch.

Mama opens the door and in walks my Daddy. He's slim and has a toasty caramel complexion with some serious waves on his head, kinda like Granddaddy's. He has thick, bushy eyebrows just like mine, full lips, beautiful eyes, and dimples just like mine. My Daddy is sharp.

Daddy begins to speak but I mind travel as I have

everything on mute because I can't believe he's here.

Not saying a word I nod my head, whisper hello and

lower my head. Mama opens the door for us and we're out;

just the two of us together, me and my Daddy. I'm relieved

because I don't have to worry about doing anything wrong.

Traveling in my mind Daddy drives and goes through every

red light and whisks me away to Missisippi but I try to

remind him I have a brother and sister to watch over.

"You want to go to the mall", he asks as I snap back.

Doing what I do best I simply nod as silence hugs me.

"Are you hungry", Daddy asks.

"No," I reply knowing that I'm hungry.

Deep down I think he knows I'm telling a story because he decides to take me to Wendy's inside the mall.

Amazed to finally be sitting face to face to the man who fathered me I can't eat. There's so much I want to tell him. For once I want to tell an adult what's going on, what I've seen, what people have done to me. I resist because I want Daddy to come back. I don't want him to think I'm a bratty tattletale. Besides, I have to see if he's loyal enough for my secrets. These secrets I carry I swear to never tell anyone because they're embarrassing, someone may get hurt and I want this visit to last forever even though I know it won't.

As darkness falls we pull up to the house most people refer to as my home but I call it the crazy house. People say Mama is crazy and I really think she's trying to make every one of us crazy too. Mr. Billy is well on his way but he's an adult. He can run and take care of himself. We can't and probably wouldn't know who to tell because they keep giving us back to her anyway.

Daddy and I say our goodbyes and here I am back in the care of Mama. Great! I'm one lucky child. That's the joke of the century. Every day I want to die but I know suicide is a sin and Grandma will be heartbroken. I want to beat Mama at taking my life. Gonna show her that I have more sense and I'm more powerful than she thinks she is but my brother and sister need me.

Death is already here. The only time I come alive is when I listen to music, I'm reading a book or looking into microscope.

Mama is drilling me on the visit and I choose to not answer much because honestly I can't remember. My visit with Daddy was a bit unusual. All I remember is him.....John Thornton Banks.....my Daddy. I don't remember hearing any sounds, nothing. It's almost like watching Grandma's TV with no sound.

"You're lying. Your Daddy told you something. What he gonna do? Try to take you away from me," she hisses.

Shaking my head I begin to part my lips but here she goes beating me again. I'm beat and thrown back into the dark room. My tears are going full speed and I feel like I'm dying because my chest is hurting bad.

"Dear Father God. Please help me. Help us. I need to get away from Mama. I love her but she don't do us right. Please send someone. Send a social worker. Make King and Tracy attack her when she feeds them. Amen." I try to close my eyes but I remember something.

"Dear God. I take that last request back. Please don't let the dogs attack Mama. I ask for forgiveness."

Grandma tells me hatred is a sin but I know Mama

sinnin' too. *Do crazy people sin?*

Having no choice but to fall asleep bruised and hurt I

think about my Daddy until my eyelids get too heavy.

Opening my eyes I see the sun shining through the

blinds. Grandma tells me no matter how bad I feel, seeing

the sun tells us that God made it shine on us and we should

be thankful and try to make the new day better than the day

before.

Rolling off the top bunk I look for Kora. Every morning

I watch her chest or pinch her to check and make sure she's

alive and breathing. *I guess I'll let her sleep and won't*

pinch her because God only knows what Mama did while I

was with Daddy. Kora is always tired and I wonder how

she manages to always stay in bed. Me, I gotta be doing

something all the time. Even if I am locked in this room, there's a whole world outside and one day I'm gonna see it. A bunch of shoes I will have just like Mama and I'm gonna dance and sing when I want to and laugh all the time without beatings.

Reaching for my notebooks and pencils I slide by the wall and peer out the window. Carefully I draw our backyard and house similar to a fire escape plan. An escape route is correct and the fire is Mama. Hiding all my drafts on the top shelf of our closet where the new clothes and shoes are kept, I only plan to show them to Kora once I'm ready to put the plan into action.

Mama's in and out the house bringing in Christmas presents. Learning to listen to everything gives me clues as to where she's located in the house. She removes the padlocks from the bedroom doors but we aren't allowed to leave. We can only go to the bathroom because she removed our metal pail we were using. On my way to the bathroom I get a glimpse that Mama has hidden lemon cookies in the linen closet and they're my favorite. Not being able to resist the temptation I sneak a cookie. Next, I peep into the hallway and sneak two more. One is for me and one is for Kora. Mitch is in his room playing with his toy cars.

"What the hell do you think you're doing", Mama yells.

Sliding my hand out of the cookie jar and replacing the glass lid I run to my room. Mama caught me red-handed and because of me everyone goes back into the dungeon.

Chapter 21

Silent night, Holy night

All is uneasy, somethings not right

I already feel like a motherless child

In the next room Mama's mind runs wild

Send your angels to protect me,

To sleep in heavenly peace.

Today is December 25, 1986 and Mama wakes us up bright and early. I'm expecting to open some gifts because after all it's Christmas. I need some dolls to talk to because Kora is getting tired of me talking her head off and my other friends who happen to be our dogs King and Tracy stay outside mostly now. The dogs seem to be on punishment too.

Mama is very religious so I guess she'll be nice on Jesus' birthday. Walking into the living room I see the Christmas tree with beautiful lights and candy canes is still up with presents underneath. Mitch, Kora and I slide under the tree and begin picking up gifts. Trying to find my name I pick up one then another. I look for Kora's name. Every present under the tree is for Mitch. Kora and I look at one other and I hug my little sister.

"Merry Christmas, Kora," I smile as I try to push her to smile. She gives me a little smirk which makes me happy. Grandma always told me that you can't miss anything you never had.

We watch Mitch open all his gifts as Mama orders us to get ready to go visit her friend Ms. Teri and her children. I'm friends with Ms. Teri's daughter, Natalie and it'll be nice to see her. We all pile up in the blue conversion van and we make our way from Hampton over to Dickerson Court in Newport News. Mr. Billy is at work as usual.

Greeted with hugs and smiles we're welcomed in. My mind is starting to travel as I'm begin to wonder what it would be like to be Ms. Teri's daughter. Snapping out of my thoughts I see that one of Ms. Teri's daughter's starts to show us her toys. Connie, the younger of the two girls, is playing with her Cabbage Patch doll. Natalie the older sister retrieves her Trouble game from under the Christmas tree. Kora is playing with Connie while Mitch has run off probably in search of food because he's greedy like that.

Sprawled out on the living room floor Natalie and I sort all the game pieces as we prepare to play with the "popomatic" bubble. This game was on my list to Santa along with a few other things Natalie has.

"You know your Mama brought these gifts over here for us," Natalie says.

Now frozen I feel like crying while the churning of my stomach and tightness of my chest make me feel as though I'm getting sick. To the bathroom I rush.

How can Mama be so mean? How can she hate us so? I have the meanest mother on earth. Mama probably thinks she's teaching us a lesson but it's not working. I just want to go home and be padlocked in the room so I can talk to God. Mama is evil.

Chapter 22

Every day is a challenge and I'm so tired. As time goes by, I'm now tired of getting beaten, tired of the stench of urine, tired of Mr. Billy working all the time. I'm tired of only eating meals at school and tired of life...but my brother and sister needs me. I have to make sure she doesn't hurt them too bad and if she does......I need to be a witness so I can run and tell.

Cutting chickens is one my duties as being the oldest child. Mama gave me strict instructions on what to do with the raw meat and at times I don't know whether we'll have a delectable meal of fried chicken or if my labor will go to the dogs once again to help make their coat shiny as Mama says.

Standing at the kitchen sink I carefully cut the carcasses in halves, quarters and even further until I have eight pieces.

How many other 11 year old's cut chickens? This is the most countriest bull I've ever heard of. They sell chickens already cut up, but knowing Mama this may be my punishment.

Today is one of our "free" times when we are not padlocked in our bedrooms. In came my brother Mitch and my mind whizzes and travels.

My Daddy knows where I live. I couldn't tell him when I was out with that I need an escape. I need to draw some attention because I know this life is not normal. Where are the social workers when you need them?

Looking at the knife I glare at the blood of the fowl on the sharp blade.

"Whatcha doin'," Mitch grins.

"Come here," I whisper. "I'm about to kill myself but don't tell Mama."

His eyes grow big and I know that he has fallen into my trap. My brother is the tattle tale ambassador himself. Within seconds I hear him blabbering to Mama. Knowing that she doesn't want anything so serious on her watch I know she'll panic and give me an outlet to let all the secrets out. Well, maybe I won't let them all out but at least Mama will be watched. This is no place for a child. I am smarter than anyone gave me credit.

When Mama tried to take my aunt and cousin Dave to court for his touches, the judge didn't believe my statement because all words were spelled correctly so they claimed

Mama could have made me write the letter but if they knew that Mama doesn't talk to me, they'd know better. My words and voice don't matter so I keep quiet maybe until I'm grown.

Wearing tight Wranglers which fit her wide hips perfectly, barefoot Mama rushed into the kitchen onto the clean, cold linoleum floor. She stares with eyes bigger than Mitch's. Her eyes stare me up and down. I keep the knife clutched in my right hand not wanting to let it go until it is safe.

"You want to kill yourself," she asks.

For a moment I freeze. This moment will determine so much and I think about the stories I enjoy in school that offer the if/then scenarios. If...then....what's going to happen?

Not knowing what to say I nod. Mama rushes and keeps me near her. She gets me ready and basically drags me outside, down the wooden steps and into the van.

She thinks Mitch told her the truth as I wonder where she's taking me. We're probably going to get help together and if we are it might be a good thing.

Feeling that things are going to get better soon, my mind races not knowing our destination. Mama drives radically as she swerves into the parking lot of Riverside Hospital. My anxiety turns to fear but I'm willing to face anything if it meant getting help.

Inside the hospital I hear Mama's rambles. I was notice everything as I am put into a bare room. Not talking much I realize I'm being transported to another place without Mama, Mitch and Kora. Not being told where I am taken I always remember to watch my surroundings just in case anything happens.

Trees are all I can see. This unknown area does not enable me to count McDonald's or 7-11 signs. That's how I identify streets and areas and I remember stores and surroundings even if I can't remember street names.

Once at our final destination I'm escorted out of the mode of transportation which was chosen to whisk me away from Mama. Mama has been traded for strangers but in my mind strangers posed less harm and always have.

The atmosphere is cold and damp because it's been raining. The gloomy weather matches how I feel inside. Now clueless as to what's going on, I choose to travel in my mind. Asking questions that are never answered do no good and talking makes me fearful. Afraid I'll say the wrong thing or expose a secret; I choose to act as if I'm mute. Talking gets me whippings and missed meals Talking gets me bloody noses, talking makes me a target and I would rather just be mute and unseen because I know there will be a day when the show will end.

Being led into an unknown building I look around as my environment kept me wondering. People are now talking, looking at me and asking questions. Looking at the floor afraid of looking into eyes I think of Mitch and Kora and wonder what they're doing.

After what I guess is routine I hear someone say the word "admitted." Words are my world and I know what that means I may have to stay for a little while. The place is cold and feels sterile. It smells cleaner than Mama's house minus our padlocked rooms. Turning away from the smells I'm escorted to a lady sitting behind an empty table.

I am asked to empty everything out of my pockets and surrender my shoestrings. One of the secrets I carry in my pockets and a little over 70 pounds I stand not wanting to empty my pockets.

"Go ahead," she motions.

Digging my wrinkled hands into my pockets with nails bitten down almost to the cuticle I retrieve bones; chicken bones to be exact. My eyes jump from the bones back to the lady as she slides a napkin onto the table which is my cue to put the bones there. Wanting to explain that I keep chicken bones I find to crack them opened with my teeth to eat the marrow. Grandma told me that the marrow has important nutrients and I figure that at least if I can't get food, nutrients would do.

Glancing up at the older white woman with glasses and a pen jotting down the few belongings I have I search her mouth and wait for words that never surface. Her thin lips remain clasped.

Looking at the kids sitting around on couches looking like they're in group therapy gives the place away. The word institution sticks out.

After relinquishing the little personal items I have on my body and depart from the bones I had eaten on a few days I'm given a gown to change into. Expecting some privacy none is given. I undressed and slipped on the gown and I wonder where it has been. I know it was probably on someone else's body yesterday. Were they crazier than I am thought to be? Now here I am in a gown going through crazy madness. Wanting to cry and at this point also wishing to undo my plan, but Grandma always told me to be careful what I wished for but I know things have to get better. She always told me there will be sunshine.

Watch me, is what they have to do. What can I possibly do? I don't really want to kill myself but if I tell them it was an escape plan they might give me back to Mama. Did someone call my Daddy? He'll probably drive through the woods and capture me from this madness. He knows I'm not crazy but I continue to remain faithful to

silence. I'm in love with silence and words. They're not a
good mix but in my mind I travel and this is life.

Chapter 23

Deemed free of harming myself, I'm now granted the privilege of being amongst peers. Studying them I know this is not a place I want to make friends nor is it place I want to stay in.

This group therapy stuff doesn't end. Do they do this every day? There's a jolly white guy with a yellow button down shirt and infamous khaki pants known to be worn by many leaders of group sessions. I know because I've been doing this therapy thing for a little over five years now. Jolly white guy seems to be grinning from ear to ear. He's the only one smiling but then again he's the only adult.

"Let us talk about why we're here," he begins.

Excellent! The man says "we" like he's one of us. I know that he gets paid to be here. He doesn't really care.

One girl with sandy blond hair is sitting on the far edge of the couch. With her left leg barely touching the floor and her right foot tucked beneath her frail frame she begins to speak.

"I don't like to eat. I won't eat because I look fat," little frail girl says. Looking out the window to the right at the bare trees she sips a nutritional drink. That explains why she's always the only person drinking from a can all the time.

Ignoring everyone I notice there is one other Black person. The other person is a boy and he looks to be younger than me. He sits stiff as a board while everyone else looks relaxed as if we're having a pajama party. This is where I have to tiptoe away from reality and travel back into my mind.

This ain't my home. I don't belong here. They're talking medication they take and the room with the padded walls, I want out of my plan.

Little stiff brown boy is beginning to talk and I want to hear what has him here.

"I tried to kill my whole family. I poured gasoline around the house....," he goes on.

Little brown boy is now zoned out. I gotta zone these people out like I do Mama. They crazy, she crazy and I'm only eleven so I just want to do normal kid stuff. This group therapy session is doing more harm than good. It doesn't me want to open up; in fact, I'm a little scared. These are the people you have to watch with one eye opened as Grandma says. I keep one eye opened with Mama and surely in this place I can't let them get close to me.

Wanting freedom from the long hallways and wooden furniture I await an escape. For the first time, I'm going to the dining hall for breakfast and I stay to myself. Devouring smells is enough for me. Afraid to eat I enjoy the smells. I smell pancakes and those fake eggs. They are not going to get me hooked on the medication I heard the kids from group therapy talk about. They may have slipped something in my food and for that reason I cannot and will not eat here.

Out of the blue someone is standing before me...zoning them out all I hear is the word court. I traveled...my life is doomed and I'll forever be known as the little girl with the crazy Mama. Will this place prove that I'm like her? They did have me talk to some doctors. I hope they won't say I'm crazy but I'm already scarred. Like Hester Prynne with the scarlet "A" which stands for adultery, I carry a letter "C." The letter "C" stands for coo-coo lady's child, crazy just like her Mama. Hopefully people will see that the only similarity is our name and I don't like that.

Court is routine and it seems as if I go to court more than I go to school. The judges are beginning to be familiar. They closed and reopened my case again and again. Even the smartest people don't have the answers and they're playing hide and go seek with my life.

Someone is being introduced to me as my social worker and I'm back in my world where I'm safe. God knows I've met my fair share of social workers and I don't remember any of their names. They all do the same thing, look at me, read over notes, and transport me and my trash bag of belongings. It's a cycle that seems to never end. The smart ones always give me back to Mama. I guess it's their job to do that because I always hear, "The best interest is with the mother." Well, they don't know my Mama. Even with the bad things they say about her doesn't compare to what she does behind closed doors.

At least while in court I learned where I'd been staying the next couple days. One of the important people that carry a briefcase said I was at Charter Colonial Institute. Jumping back into real life right before the judge hits the gavel I hear a series of words, 'Custody' and the 'Hampton Department of Social Services'.

Remembering the conversation my new social worker and I had before going into the courtroom, he asked me a question I had never been asked before.

"Who do you want to live with, your mother or your father," was what the social worker asked.

Looking at the floor, chin tucked and wanting them to figure out what I was trying to say I whispered.

"Whoever treats me the best," were my exact words. They should be able to tell that with Mama's track record she doesn't treat me the way I need to be.

"Why do you want to live with your mother," was the next question.

Not really having a reason I spit out one.

"I need to make sure Mama takes her medicine and I need to help take care of my brother and sister."

Guessing that I must have said the magic words, I'm back in the system.

White car, circular emblem bearing the state of Virginia seal, trash bags, my little belongings are the pieces to the puzzle today. These cars cause so much embarrassment and I'm now at an age where I have to scan my surroundings to ensure that no one my age sees me getting out of a social services car. Riding in the car means I belong to the state, which actually means I'm not worth anything but a bunch of papers they call records and the check they hand over to my foster parents.

Mrs. Bertram is my newest parent's name. Not wanting to say much I know I'm going to be here temporarily because I hear them say emergency placement.

Daddy is in and out of the hospital fighting cancer but he keeps constant contact with the Hampton Department of Social Services and he's now fighting to get custody of me. It's been revealed that Mama intercepted Daddy's attempts of getting custody of me before. She acted as if he vanished and never wanted me but that wasn't the truth.

Prayer is keeping me strong and I pray for Daddy to get well. I ask God to give me all the pain because I'm used to it. Court is pain, Mama is pain and pain is found in breathing and waking up feeling worthless everyday but I know God hears my prayers no matter how bad things may

seem.

There's another court date and it's now time to leave

Mrs. Bertram. I don't feel anything because I know nothing

is felt for me. I can always tell if they care. Previous foster

parents gave me advice and attempted to teach me a lesson

or two. Nothing was learned, nothing to remember but a

name and that she'll receive payment for my room and

board.

Chapter 24

He's a man, surely different from the other social workers. My new social worker is a man and his name is Keith Davis. Checking him out from head to toe, I notice everything, his dark skin, glasses and razor bumps just like my stepfather Mr. Billy. He has on some tight tweed pants and brown penny loafers they're beat like they're his only pair.

Pennies? Nope, he doesn't have any pennies. I always check to see if loafers have pennies and none are in his shoes so to me it means one of two things. Mr. Davis is either poor like me or he doesn't care about his appearance. He's not fashionable as they would say.

Now sitting in the front seat of the government car my seat belt is hugging me tighter than any human ever has.

I have to watch this one close. He might be one of those

sick men wanting to touch young girls like me. Maybe he

knows I like to be silent and watch everything. Maybe the

other ones touched me because they knew I was friends

with silence and I'm afraid to tell so the secrets pile up.

Pulling up to an odd yellow house I can tell these people

are old. Older people always like screened in front porches.

The house also has a makeshift wooden gate that's rotting.

I'm guessing a big house probably for a lot of kids which

mean a lot of checks.

Walking to the house I observe the bricks laying in the

yard as well as the landscape. No flowers equal, no

happiness. Nothing is here to remind me of Grandma

except the porch only Grandma's doesn't have a screen.

The sound of bedroom slippers dragging the floor draws

near and before Mr. Davis has the chance to knock, out

comes a short light skinned woman, with freckles popping

chewing gum. She looks me up and down without a smile.

.   The gap between her teeth is very noticeable and I

notice she has one that's rotting and a gold one on the other

side. She draws a lot of attention to her mouth for her teeth

not to be straight and white; poor thing.

Grandma would follow that by saying, "Bless her heart.

We gonna pray for her. She probably don't know no

better."

Ms. Snagapuss is holding the front door as if she's

guarding her life with is. She's sorta round and she matches

my new social worker because her fashion sense is also

missing. Along with the noisy slippers she probably got

from the dollar store she has on sweat pants and a tattered,

colorful house coat.

So this is how they dress for company at this house.

"This is Janera and she will be here for the night," said Mr. Davis

Not paying much attention to my new warden because we only have to deal with one another for 24 hours, I'm shown to what is called my bedroom aka my cell. I'm now doing time in foster care for now.

Chapter 25

Settling into the dark, damp smelling room I observe my surroundings as usual. Nothing is out of the norm. The carpet is dark gray and looks to be the industrial kind used in offices. There's a dresser to my left and one to my right by the window beside the bed. Looking at the bed I wonder who else has slept there. I hate sleeping on sheets not knowing if anyone's changed them. At least respect me enough to change the sheets.

The furnishings are outdated but at least they have them. I hate sleeping in the dark. I bet they didn't put that in my records. Janera Braswell...check...crazy mother...check...therapy sessions...check...afraid of the dark...not checked.

As I walk to the window I pull the curtains back to see the sun. Grandma taught me to always look to the sun.

Look to God, she says. Most of the time when I look to the sun, I recite my Bible verse I had to memorize while living with Mama. *Psalm 121:1, I will look to the hills from which cometh my strength.* My mind always clings to that verse. I was told to recite it whenever I need strength or direction.

The sun feels good to me right now although the room feels gloomy. My garbage bag of clothes is still on the floor.

I'm just here overnight; it'll be back over my shoulder tomorrow to get in that little white embarrassing car with the emblem.

Not wanting to sit on the bed I study the dresser beside the window and notice everything on it. There's an eight track player, sports magazines and a bunch of cards. I'm not interested in sport cards unless they have Scott Hamilton on them. Those are probably baseball cards but moving closer I see they're Garbage Pail Kids cards. There looks to be a couple hundred cards. Rotten Ralph, Barfin Barbara, etc..... Laughing at the disgusting characters that looked to be Cabbage Patch Kids, my mind forgot that I'm in a loaner home. My mind forgets that I'm just traveling and I'm a child gypsy.

In this home I keep quiet because there's a lot to digest. Just a few days ago I was in a loony bin for kids, went to court and now here I am in another home. I need to scope out my new home.

Mrs. Jacobs aka Snagapuss has burst into the room and interrupts my enjoyment of Garbage Pail Kids to tell me dinner is ready. As I'm led from the room that I'll be sleeping in, we walked through another room with lots of books. I don't know what they call it because I know it's not the living room but I choose to call it the library. Mrs.

Jacobs has the biggest book shelves I've ever seen in a home.

I can only imagine the words that are waiting for me in the books. There are humongous windows and there's a lot of sunlight even though the blinds are closed. There's a bar to the right. Mama has a bar and she loves to drink Canadian Mist.

To the left there's a china cabinet and across from it is where all the books live. Behind the bookshelves there's an area with a contemporary looking white leather couch.

This is a nice genuine leather couch and it doesn't match the other furnishings that look to have leaped from the 1970's into 1987.

Moving on I admire the wall behind the couch which is donned with mirrors reaching the ceiling. I can tell Mrs. Jacobs loves plants because they're everywhere.

I like the art on the walls too. These people might have just a little taste after all. Hopefully I'll be able to sit in the library during my 24 hour stay.

Passing through what I call the library to get to the kitchen I stop to read a sign. It's actually a place to hang keys but there's writing and the word shenanigans stick out to me. There are red and yellow dogs on it that resembled Droopy the cartoon character. But I must remember the word. Hmmm.... I have to look up this new word as I tuck it into my mental safe.

The kitchen is small and for the house to be so big I'm surprised at the size of the kitchen. There are regular kitchen appliances; a microwave, refrigerator, stove and I notice there's a television over the microwave and even more plants.

"You eat pork chops?" Mrs. Jacobs asks.

"Yes, ma'am," I reply not making eye contact with the woman.

On the table there's a plate with pork chops, macaroni and cheese and cabbage. It smells and looks good and it's been a while since I've had a good "hot" meal. I've been munching on the cookies that were given to me from the vending machine after court.

Mrs. Jacobs looks at me over her bifocals.

As long as she keeps looking at me I'm surely not to eat. I don't like people watching me eat.

Sliding onto the chair Mrs. Jacobs says nothing to me as she takes her plate with her into her bedroom. The sound of her bedroom slippers fade as she walks further down the hallway away from the kitchen.

Taking the first bite, I close my eyes and imagine that I really live here and Mama has prepared the food.

The front door slams and has caused me to snap out of the world inside my head. Looking up at teenage boy standing over me I scan him. Dark skin and kinda bow legged; he looks like he's been playing in dirt all day with a torn t-shirt.

"Ma, who 'dis girl," he yells towards Mrs. Jacobs bedroom.

Bedroom slippers are now coming towards the kitchen.

"Lewis, why you gotta holler? You see the girl trying to eat her food." I'm used to being called the girl or her or just she actually it's the same as little Janera. People don't really know me. They know about Mama and her crazy ways but they never really pay attention to me.

"Her name is Janera and she'll be staying here until tomorrow. Janera, this is my youngest son Lewis."

I glance up at the boy and quickly look away. Feeling

small like a toy solider I feel like a freak in a freak show.

Come one, come all. Come see the girl with the crazy

Mama. She lives in her head because no one talks to her,

she has an imagination out of this world and she knows

some amazing words and lives life through music. Step

right on up.

Out of my thoughts I hop as I'm now back at the kitchen

table eating dinner.

Feeling uneasy sitting at the strange table, I want

tomorrow to come quickly. I always feel as if I'm invading

the space of others because nothing is ever mine.

Everything is always theirs and I'm just allowed to use it.

After taking my bath in the strange tub, in the strange

bathroom, in this strange house I now face the bed.

Turning back the covers there are white sheets with orange and red stripes to match the orange blanket. Looking closely, the sheets appear to be clean. Inspecting them I don't see any crumbs nor do I see any wrinkles from a previous body that may have occupied the bed prior to my 24 hour visit.

It's safe just a little but I'm still afraid of the dark. Not being able to sleep I keep my eyes wide opened as I lay anxiously praying and asking God to send the little white government car sooner than later.

Chapter 26

Waking up in the house feels strange and I don't get a good feeling about the people here either. I'm glad that I'm about to make a break. After being told to get ready for the day I do as I am told by Mrs. Jasper. I don't like the way they look at me. Mrs. Jasper is always looking over those eyeglasses as if her nose is in the air. I don't know what her problem is. My teeth are white and straight so she needs to look straight through those Sandford and Son bifocals and take a look in the mirror.

Mr. Davis is on time and he's asking Mrs. Jasper the usual questions. At this point I think I know most of social worker's language. When he stands with his black leather briefcase that houses his yellow legal pad and pens, and some other papers he tucks the infamous manila folder under his arm. Knowing that's my cue for our exit, I stand to grab my black trash bag that holds everything I own, my life's savings. Trying to be kind he takes the bag for me as I say goodbye to Mrs. Jasper.

Well here's to another home off my checklist. I'll never see this place again, off to court we go.

Court went so fast and I'm back in the white car. I guess this is the life God has for me right now. Tears still come sometimes but there's so much to get my attention so the pain is beginning to not hurt that bad. In my mind is where I choose to live and dance and read books and I laugh a lot because the people who think they're hurting me ain't so great themselves. I see everything and I remember so much. Everyone wants me to talk and open up. If I really start opening up some people are going to be in deep trouble but I don't even know who's who anymore because Social Services act like Mama bad and they know what she does. They know she won't take her medicine and they keep sending me back to her and each time it gets worst. I

hope they never send me back there ever again. I haven't

heard where Mitch and Kora are yet.

Mr. Davis looks at me and tells me I'm going to be

returning to Mrs. Jacob's home. Playing with silence I look

out the window at the trees and count droplets of water on

the window. Don't matter to me where I go because what I

want doesn't matter. This is just called my life but I'm not

gonna start living until I'm 18 and free. I'm gonna run free

and no one is going to ask me what I'm smiling for. No

home of my home and people who want to take my smile

away and ask what I'm smiling for. I smile because I can.

"We're waiting for the ok to send you to Mississippi to

live with your father."

Hearing that news makes the ride better and I cheer up.

I'm not gonna be completely happy until I can see my

Daddy and they stop calling me a ward of the state. That's

not my name. My name is Janera Braswell. They make me

feel like I'm in jail for real. Ward is similar to warden.

State and government go hand in hand then there's jail.

I'm a prisoner. If they take the time to understand me

they'll know that I feel they just have a job to do.

Pulling up to Mrs. Jacob's house I retrieve the bag once

again. This time I'm not a visitor but I sure hope they get

things situated in Mississippi for me real soon. It makes me

feel good that someone wants me. Daddy is stepping up to

claim this lost girl. Mr. Davis tells me my father will call

the Jacob's home later in the day to speak to me. Makes me

feel like Christmas.

Going back into the room I had slumbered the previous

night, Mrs. Jasper asked me to empty my belongings from

the trash bag and put them in the dresser drawers. My

clothes have never been in dresser drawers. I'm used to

trash bags and boxes. Even Mama did weird things with

our clothes I didn't understand. She kept our clothes and had brand new clothes for us in closets but we were not allowed to wear them. Probably has something to do with the court keep calling her unfit.

The few items I have in the bag are not enough to fill the entire dresser. Mrs. Jacobs assists me and she holds up my clothes as if they're rags and there she goes with that frowning again. My clothes are all I have and they're mine, they're good enough for me. Grandma told me that no matter what you have, take good care of it and as long as it's clean that's all that matters.

"I'm going to ask Mr. Davis for a voucher so I can get you some new clothes," Snagapuss says.

Never knew foster parents could do that. No one ever gets me new clothes except the lady I stayed with when I was six and the Brown's, the couple I hear that Mitch lives with now. Aunt Anne got all our clothes from the thrift store and said they were just fine except for those bell-bottoms I was forced to wear. I think I was the only seven year old wearing bell-bottoms in 1982 when the rest of the world was rocking Jordache.

After putting my clothes away I ask permission to sit in the library. Studying the bookshelves I found they have a collection of encyclopedias and only families with money can afford an updated collection of Encyclopedia Britannica. Looking at the volumes I'm giddy with excitement because I love to read and I'm tired of reading the same Judy Blume books I have. I love living in Fudge's world but it's time for something new. Fudge's brother Peter is growing up and so am I.

My in-home library session was interrupted by Snagapuss.

"Chile, you don't need to be stuck up in this house. Gone outside and play," she barks.

I do have my roller skates so I fish them out and go

outside.

Outside I'm automatically given the title of the new girl

and people want to know who I am, where I came from and

how long I'll be staying. Questions I don't think I can or

want to answer.

There's a girl who lives across the street and her name is

Bianca and although she's younger she looks older than

me. She's developed and the older women say, and I'm not.

At eleven, I'm 72 pounds and definitely flat chested; flat as

a board. I pray to God that I'll blossom soon because

everyone is wearing training bras and I'm still in tank tops

with no bumps. There's nothing to hold up because I'm all

chest, flat chest.

Bianca even acts older but I'm used to that. Maybe being

locked away in closets and bedrooms caused me to lose

track of time so I gotta catch up where I left off but

sometimes I don't want to. I'm ok in my world except for

my flat chest. Gotta get some titties and I'll be just fine.

Chapter 27

Months go by with the Jasper's and life becomes nothing but life. I'm used to this foster care stuff now. Keeping my room clean is hard but I achieve it most days. My job is to go to school, keep my room clean and also keep the rest of the house tidy. I try to keep the kitchen clean but I never seem to wash the dishes to Mrs. Jasper's liking. There's always a morsel stuck to a plate or a pot with grease. The dishes aren't my favorite but I look for anything to escape. Standing at the sink I slip in and out of my mind with thoughts of things that had happened to me before. I like to reenact things as if I actually have a voice, pretending to say everything that's in my head and my heart. Doing laundry also allows me to get lost. The clothes line gives me a lot of time out in the sun. Deep down I know things will get better. Physically and mentally I'm in jail and I can't wait or the day to be free.

Mrs. Jasper moved my room down the hall beside her bedroom and I like it better because there's more sunlight. The new room doesn't have a damp odor and the color of the wood paneling is lighter, similar to pine. There's one dresser and two twin beds with red bedspreads. The room was smaller but I don't need a lot of room anyway. Choosing the bed closest to the wall because of the window I smiled. The window on the side had a silver radiator beneath it. It was an eyesore to me because it reminded me of Mama and the rooming house we lived in.

Daddy calls me a lot and I live for conversations with him. Privacy was what I demanded when I talked to him. Whenever Snagapuss yells (she does that often) to tell me Daddy is on the phone I take the rotary phone from the kitchen and plug it into the jack beside my bed. Lying on my bed is what I do during our conversations and I'm happy someone actually calls me.

Daddy and I laugh together, pray together and he doesn't make me feel ashamed of who I am and he never makes me feel bad about Mama. Wishing it went both ways because Mama dogged my Daddy and I found that it was all lies. He promises me that he's gonna get me.

"Sweetheart, tell me what do you want," he said.

"All I want is to live with you, Daddy," I replied.

I wanted to play jump rope with him and I wanted him to cheer me on as I skate. He tells me that he'll get me anything I want and I believe him.

"Daddy, can I tell you something," I asked.

"Baby, you can tell me anything."

"Daddy, remember that day we went to court and me, Mama, and Mr. Billy were sitting behind you? Well I'm sorry I didn't speak to you that day. Mama told me I would get in trouble if I did. I'm sorry you came all the way from Mississippi and we didn't spend any time together. I also apologize for Mama laughing about your hair. I'm sorry." I begin to cry.

"Sweetheart, you have nothing to apologize for. I want to you always remember that I'm your father and I've loved you since day one. Never let anyone tell you any different. I know your mother made you not speak to me but that's fine. That was then, all that matters is now and I need you to stop crying."

Wiping my tears I don't want to waste all our time with me crying. We talk about my dreams because Daddy is the only one who listens and tells me I can do anything. He tells me I'm very smart and he wants nothing but the best for me.

Going to school I daydream about Daddy and the day we'll be reunited. I can't concentrate on much unless it's art or music. At home there's no one to help me with homework so most of the time I don't do it. I don't care about much anymore. Day by day I just wake and follow the flow. This is life.

I have chores to do and when I'm not doing chores I'm reading or teach myself a new craft. I taught myself to cross-stitch and love it because it makes time go by fast. I'm trying to learn macramé but it's kind of tricky. Fashion is cool to me but Snagapuss dresses me like she wants. I want to pick out my own clothes like the ones I draw.

No one talks to me so I read and learn whatever interests me. Whenever I get money, what I don't spend at Highs Ice Cream parlor across the street goes to my hobby. Going outside is fun and I play with friends I've made in the neighborhood but I like my peace; in my bedroom getting kissed by the sun while reading or listening to music. My mind doesn't race when I craft or read and music takes me to other places.

Mrs. Jasper yells too much and it's beginning to get on my nerves. I swear sometimes I see old Snagapuss' tonsils. I imagine Billy Jean King coming to my rescue hitting her right in the mouth with a tennis ball shutting her up until eternity. I bet she doesn't know she has a chipped tooth. I'd keep my mouth closed if my tooth looked like that.

I'm beginning to have mixed feelings about Mrs. Jasper. I'm appreciative of her allowing me to stay in her home and she does things other foster parents don't do like cook nice meals, take me along on family outings on Fridays and takes the time to take me shopping. Our shopping trips mean a lot because for the first time in my life I have decent clothes from stores other than K-Mart or the thrift store. Daddy was the first person to buy me anything out of the mall but Mrs. Jasper was the only foster parent who shopped for me at the mall.

I wonder if she loves me because she takes time to get me sized for my training bras even though her son Lewis says she has to knit one because I had no breasts.

Life at the Jaspers offers privacy which I consider a luxury. I don't really fit into this world or maybe the people I'm with just won't let the real me shine. My corniness, thirst for knowledge, stubborn nature, creative energy, free heart is different to a lot of people but it makes sense to me. Different they call me, why I don't know.

My daily reading material is being drawn to a halt by knocks on my bedroom door. In walks a tall dark skinned, older man wearing utility pants and a white t-shirt. He has beady eyes and a thick mustache. Jumping from my bed I make sure I'm presentable.

"Hiya doin. Christine, my wife told me you'd be staying with us for a little bit. I'm a long distance truck driver and I'm hardly home but you'll see me from time to time," said the strange man.

"Hello. It's nice to meet you," is all I say. Men scare me because they always look at me in strange ways. He smiles and although uneasy I slide a small grin and rush to shake his hand. His hand is really big and I hope he doesn't notice my sweaty palms. Studying him, I see that he needs to earn my trust. There's something behind his eyes I can't quite put a finger on.

Every day I exist because I know I'll have a life once Daddy sends for me. The custody battle seems to be quite long but I count the days like I'm in jail as I continue to attend school and therapy sessions. Therapy buys me time away from chores and the hollering and I hope that on the way from one of my sessions someone will not take me back to the Jaspers but will whisk me away to Biloxi, MS.

Drifting through life is what I'm doing. At school I'm the class clown but at home I'm Cinderella. Mrs. Jasper is now comfortable hitting me for my wrongdoings I guess because I never told after the first time. I don't say anything because the beatings aren't as bad as Mama's and the custody battle is underway so I loan her my body to beat but my mind and heart are already in Biloxi with Daddy.

My new friends also take my mind away from the house. They come over and knock on the door to see if I'm able to go outside so we can create dance routines. My love for music and dance encourages me to have an interest in wanting to become a cheerleader but Mrs. Jasper told

Mr. Davis I need to bring my grades up. How am I

supposed to do that when I have no help? I try my best but

it's not enough so I settle for dance steps to Salt N Pepa's

Tramp and Wipeout by The Fat Boys.

Allison, my friend from down the street, is a great

dancer and she teaches me every single dance step. I

always master them right except the time we tried to flip

off the chair against the tree to Janet Jackson's Pleasure

Principle. Not only did I bust my butt, I found that you get

nasty scrapes and cuts when falling on a tree trunk.

To me, Allison has grown to be my best friend. She's a

couple years older, has dark skin, long skinny legs and she

wears a Jheri curl. I dream of having a curl so I roll my

hair really tight to try to pull off the same effect. Old

Snagapuss has cheap Avon hair products so my curls are

always dry and frizzy. I long for the drip effect Allison has but Snagapuss says that curls are not for me. She doesn't know anything.

Allison and I love to imitate hairstyles we find in Word Up and Right On magazines. Pepa changes her hair all the time and I know for sure I'll never get permission to dye my hair. I love Salt N Pepa, so I plaster their pictures all over my walls along with Big Daddy Kane, Heavy D., Bell Biv Devoe, Roxanne Shante and Al. B. Sure just to name a few.

Aside from the beatings, the many chores and an occasional touches from my foster brothers; life is ok. Daddy is on my mind and all this other stuff will be a thing of the past soon.

Chapter 28

It's a week before my birthday and Mr. Davis has come to visit unexpectedly. As usual I'm in my room reading and I hear Mrs. Jasper call me. Running into the library Snagapuss is standing by the bar and Mr. Davis is sitting on the white leather sofa and he has on those brown pants again and his loafers still don't possess any pennies.

"Janera, I have something important to tell you," Mr. Davis looks away.

"Thank you Jesus. I'm going to Daddy, I think as I search his eyes for excitement but there's none.

All of a sudden both set of eyes are on me. Wondering what's going on I begin to panic and sweat. Sweaty palms please go away. This isn't a good feeling.

Opening his mouth Mr. Davis says the words very clearly, "Your father lost his battle with cancer. He passed away yesterday."

Everything is getting fuzzy and I feel lightheaded like I'm going to faint but I refuse to let them see me fall. I can't say anything and don't want to; all I can do is run. Running down the hallway to my room enables six footsteps to turn into three miles. Onto the orange bedspread I leap as I release my tears. I know I'm going to wake up. This can't be happening.

Daddy told me he'll never leave me but the last time I talked to him he was in the hospital and he said he'd be ok and was going to get better. Crying for hours in my room, no one bothers me and I don't think I like anyone anymore. I hate everyone because it's just me against the world. No one understands me. The sun appears to be hiding; I think the sun knows that it's a sad day in my world so the sun allowing me time to cry. Grandma said that I'm connected to a different energy and maybe she's right because even the sun knows I need a break today. Thank you, God!

After finding the strength I fall onto my knees in prayer.

"God please help me. I need you. My Daddy is gone and you know I need somebody. Please help me because I need somebody to care. What am I supposed to do now? I want my Daddy. I want my Daddy. Please give me my Daddy back. I'm begging you" I sob until I fall into a slumber.

Waking up I realize it's a new day and I still don't care about anything. Nothing matters anymore because Daddy died and a part of me has died too. I feel numb and block things out. I'm not going to let people know my hurt. My relationship with Daddy shielded me from things but with him being out of the picture I know I'm now fair game.

The state is not going to take care of me like Daddy.

They never say the same words. Their words come from books, briefcases, yellow legal paper and court documents. Now that my hero is gone I know the beatings and touches will get worse. Disconnected from our phone calls, everyone knows I don't have anyone else to tell.

The only other people I talk to who are related to me other than Daddy are my Aunt Mattie and my cousin Karen. Aunt Mattie called to tell me she was sorry to hear about Daddy dying. She said she's known him from back in the day because they both grew up in Newport News, where all of my family is from. Mama's side of the family and Daddy's side are from downtown Newport News.

Aunt Mattie never talks badly about my Dad and she refers to him as Banks. She tells me he was great and she is correct. She also told me he was a good man when he was living so I know she isn't just saying it to make me feel better. Aunt Mattie tells me the truth whether I want to know or not. She always tells me that a man's word is his bond.

Days after Mr. Davis delivered the bad news he's here again.

What does he want now? Things can't possibly get worse. This time he has a something wrapped up in foil. Finding that Aunt Mattie has baked me a birthday cake and sent it to social services makes me smile. That woman knows how to get to me. I sit the cake on the bar and just looked at it in amazement.

I'm now about to be twelve and this is my second birthday cake ever. Grandma made me one when I was younger. Mama never gave me a cake but she did give me an oatmeal pie one night on my birthday as she rushed out of the door. Clinging to her mahogany leather boot I had begged her to stay with me at Grandma's house, but she decided whatever on the other side of the door was better. Out of her pocket she slid a Little Debbie oatmeal pie to sooth my cries.

Aunt Mattie and Granddaddy always talked about putting love into cooking so I know it's nothing but love sitting on the bar in the form of a cake. The cakes' frosting is pink and it also has green leaf shaped cookies all over it with chocolate Hershey Kisses everywhere. Aunt Mattie has an imagination just like mine because I've never seen anything like it before. An original work of art is what Grandma calls it; abstract. Too pretty to slice, I admire the cake sitting on the bar as I walk in and out of the library to do chores or talk on the phone.

Before Daddy passed away he suggested that I continue to pray and attend church regularly. Conveniently there's a church across the street and I go without anyone asking me to. I have my very own Bible that I tuck under my right arm and strut across the street every Sunday morning. Church is where I'm safe from touches and beatings. I even join three choirs because I love, love, love music.

Now that Daddy's gone things are worse but I spend more and more time at the church to escape the Jasper's home. Not able to trust anyone, I pray to God about my secrets but I feel like they're driving me crazy a little. Between the things I don't tell and the goings on of the home social services placed me in, I wonder if I can wait until age 18. Seven years and I'll be done for good with the system.

Chapter 29

With Daddy gone there are no other options as far as a happy home. Mr. Davis has made it clear that people don't want kids my age. They want babies and younger children he says because they're easier to manage and don't cause much trouble he says.

At the age of 12 I'm a devoted church member and Sunday is my favorite day of the week and it sets the tone for my week. When Monday comes I exist once again, drift and wait for Sunday. The only thing to look forward to on weekdays is reading, music, eating and Oprah Winfrey after school. I watch her because she gets people to talk about many things, she's not afraid to wear bright colors and she's always changing her hair. If and when I miss a day of school, I watch Sally Jesse Rahpael as she wears those unique bright red eyeglasses.

People tell me I have an old soul or whatever that means. They say I act older; mature they call it. If they had to take care of brothers and sisters, learn Mama like the backs of their hands, I think they'd know why I'm a bit older with my thinking. I gotta be fast even when they say I'm slow with my physical movement I'm swift in my head. That's where I live, think, and draw out scenarios, design things and escape. I do a lot of traveling.

As I put the tea kettle on the stove and prepare for a cup of tea I find a place at the outdated kitchen table which is my makeshift throne. I can't believe this lady Oprah Winfrey is opening up about the abuse she encountered as a child. She gives me hope that maybe one day I'll be able talk too. She's brave and most of the time people don't talk much about terrible things unless they go to therapy or

court.

On Sundays after morning church service it's Julia

Child who captivates me on PBS and takes me to the world

of cooking. Hearing her *Bon apatite* salutation makes my

day. Her accent is interesting and her stories are amazing.

One day I will cook like Julia Child and when I'm

grown I will tell my husband and children that it was Julia

Child who taught me to stuff a chicken; only I'll be gentle

with my fowl. Julia handles her food as if she's been tag

teamed by Rick Flair. That is a sign of a strong woman.

Maybe I'll write her and tell her that the chicken is already

dead. She needs a column just like Ann Landers.

Sundays when I return home from church and I try to

guess what Mrs. Jasper is cooking. It always smells good

but now to me old Snagapuss is just a mean old woman

with no joy. If she talked to me I'd ask her to read the

comics or Ann Landers with me or learn something from Julia Child. Maybe we could sew together since we both like clothes. Her clothes a little bit old fashioned but together we could do some things but she doesn't talk to me only at me.

Being that my imagination is big as the sea like Granma says, I make things out of almost anything. Mrs. Jasper is away visiting family members in NC and while she's away I make sure I spend as much time away from the house as possible.

I wonder why she leaves me home with her husband and sons. Does she think nothing happens when she's gone? Well, I don't have time to ponder that because I have to keep my mind busy or I might just go crazy one day and I refuse to let that happen. People think I'll be like Mama but they're wrong.

Finding a wooden stick I paint it pretty lime green with the paint I found on the back porch as I was finished hanging laundry at the clothesline. Glitter sparkles are added as the finishing touch. Not quite sure what I just made I put it on the cement step of the back porch to dry as we await the return of the lady of the house.

"What is it," Mrs. Jasper asks.

Still trying to figure out what I had made, silence creeps in and causes me to freeze. It's pretty and I just want to show her that I can be a good girl even though I'm bad at school and I can make pretty things.

"It's a...ummmm... a bookend," I say quickly. "See you do it like this."

Holding the stick as long as my forearm horizontally I show her how to use it.

"You make sure the glitter is up towards the sun." I begin to smile because my idea starts to make sense. Quick thinking is what I tapped in to as the stick was drying.

She's looking at the top of her glasses now and she's probably figuring that it's just an old stick that I found but Grandma always told me you can find beauty in anything. I don't care what Snagapuss thinks because I can imagine and create anything I want. You have to have a huge imagination to live in this house.

She smiles but it's a crooked one. Rarely seeing her smile I accept it and go to my room and escape into my world and read.

Washing dishes is not my favorite chore and Mrs. Jasper doesn't realize the reason the dishes are always dirty is because I rush to do them. Whenever I'm in the kitchen I'm felt on, rubbed, humped, and kissed. My two foster brothers both secretly behind one another backs do things to me. Lewis isn't as bad because he just grinds on me. Rolling my eyes toward the ceiling I hold my breath, count down and zone out.

Moe on the other hand is more aggressive. His touches aren't just confined to the kitchen. He grabs and pushes me onto beds, yanks and hits me as he bends me over couches but he never gets in. Prayer, thoughts of Daddy and Grandma and Aunt Mattie's words keep me strong in this house. I pray every day that God will help me remain a virgin until marriage. A foster brother shouldn't love a sister in nasty ways. Confusion is everywhere because they beat and ridicule me in the open and touch me in the dark when no one is around. I don't know what or how to feel anymore.

Used to the touches, they are now as routine as church, school, Oprah Winfrey and Julia Child. Knowing what to do on cue I zone out many things and look at the imaginary clock in my mind. Wishing the age 18 would come sooner than later and hopes that I won't be ruined as the old folks say.

Although I'm used to the touches there is one touch that appears foreign to me. Standing in the kitchen, Mr. Jasper is home off of the road and he's standing by the key chain holder with the dogs on it.

"Come here Janera."

Mr. Jasper had gained my trust because Mrs. Jasper doesn't beat me much when he's home because he defends me.

"You shouldn't make that child clean so much. She's not a maid," he'd say.

I think she hates me for that reason but I can't say anything. He's right but I think she hates that her husband goes against her in front of company as well. His efforts make me marked.

"She's a good girl and does what she's told most of the time," he'd tell company in reference to me.

As I walk over to him I can smell his cologne. Mr. Jasper is older but he was a very clean man. After I get myself together in the bathroom in the mornings he was next in line. Some mornings he beats me to the bathroom and if I go in after him I can always tell that he has shaved. He's almost as clean as my Daddy. No one will ever compare to John Thornton Banks.

Looking up at him wearing those same gray work pants and white t-shirt I looked into his eyes because at this point I trust him.

"Yes sir," I murmur.

"I know you and your Daddy talked a lot and I'm sorry he's gone," he began to say. I begin to think Mr. Jasper is my favorite person in the house.

"I'll be your Daddy now. You know I have daughters too. Come kiss me like my daughters kiss me," he continued.

Puzzled because his daughters don't live in the home and they're grown women and I only see them kiss him on his cheek. Why does he want me to kiss him on the cheek? I never have before. Beginning to escape in my mind I freeze and just stand still. Mr. Jasper put his big hands around my small waist and pulled me close to him. All I can see are lips and whiskers, or a mustache as most people say.

I pray and drift. *"He's one of them. He did all those things for me to like him just for this day. He wants what every man wants. He likes to kiss and touch young girls,"* I begin to come back.

Lips are mushy and wet and I don't kiss back but try to push away.

"Please God don't let his fake teeth slip out of his mouth into mine," I silently prayed.

Mr. Jasper tries looking me in the eyes and quickly I look out of the kitchen window to the right. I'm now dead. I died right after Daddy did but no one noticed. My body remains here but my soul is dead......gone. God sent angels to revive me and I listen but I still feel dead inside.

Since my foster father now kisses me I fall so deep into my world everyone is left wondering what's wrong with me. Whenever Mr. Davis visits I hope he sees that my eyes always lay on the carpet. I want him to see that I have been so hurt and don't feel like living. Who cares anyway?

Everybody is messed up. HELP ME GOD!!!!!

Chapter 30

I'm a mute at home not saying much until I'm around my friends. At home I'm a victim and at school the perpetrator. They touch me at home and I touch them at school with my fists or the palms of my hand.

Wythe Elementary School is directly across the street. Walking to school every day gives me time to think. Mrs. Harris is one of my favorite teachers but I'll never tell her. She pulls me aside and tells me that I'm more than the blows I gave. She tells me she knows I'm smart. I know everything she tells me is true but I can't concentrate at school when I have to wonder about what's going to happen when I get home.

All my positive thoughts surround Daddy and I take his picture with me everywhere but Mr. Davis says it's normal.

"Is it not normal for a little girl to long for her Daddy because he looked like the sun and now he's gone and there's so much darkness in her life. Is it normal for my social worker to visit me and sometimes I never say one word. I wish he'd just take me away for not talking but then again according to him there is no other place for me to go. Daddy dead and Mama will never have me again. Mr. Davis is just as stupid as those papers he pretends to look at. Everybody stupid, they pretend to look out for the best interest of the child and I don't like anyone but my friends and the people at my church." The best interest of the child; I hear those words too much and basically they really don't mean anything.

Mrs. Harris has my attention and I can't let her know she's the best part of my day and I daydream about what it would be like to be her daughter, even if she is white and has a tomboy haircut. She shows me attention my foster mother Mrs. Jasper neglects to. Mrs. Harris taught me about kumquat trees and she even has one in the classroom. At Mrs. Jaspers I have to care for the plants but she doesn't talk to me about them. I just give them water, talk to them and check on them daily to see which ones need more water and which ones don't. Mrs. Harris told me (actually the whole class) where kumquats come from, how to care from them and we even get the chance to taste them.

My fifth grade teacher is also teaching me how important the election of 1988 is. We're having a mock election and I plan to vote for Michael Dukakis. She teaches me about cumulus and stratus clouds and we make weathervanes which is interesting. Wanting to open up to

Mrs. Harris I feel I can't but I almost came close one day.

After one of my outbursts she takes me out to the

hallway.

"Ok, Janera. Tell me what's going on. What's wrong,"

she asks as she stoops down to get eye level with me.

"Nothing. I ain't doing nothing," I say looking at the

speckled, marble floor of the hallway.

In my mind I say, "Mrs. Harris, I want you to be my

Mama and I don't care that we have a different skin color.

We can save all the milk cartons at school and make a ton

of weather vanes when we go home. I'll help you find

another cute hairstyle just like Pepa so you won't look like

a brunette Dennis the Menace. Maybe you'll like an MC

Lyte hairstyle. You help me and I'll help you. Let's do

that thing called cooperation you always telling me about."

Instead of opening up to my teacher I continue to act

out. One of my classmates is a troublemaker and he's been

getting on my nerves since second grade.

Walking past my desk as I try to concentrate, Manny the

troublemaker smacks my paper onto the floor. Speechless I

get up, walk over to him, clench my teeth and start beating

him. Not caring what strength he has I go through too

much at home to come to school and be bullied.

Mrs. Harris tries to stop me but I can't. My mind won't

let my hands be free. By the time I realize what's going on

things are bad I've slammed Manny and Mrs. Harris

against the door to gain control. Mrs. Harris shudders in

pain and I stopped. Freezing and I realize I have possibly

hurt my tomboy Mama.

My teacher needs medical attention and now I'm

ashamed. Classmates look to me for a laugh and excitement

sometimes which is my release from home but never did I

think I'd ever seriously hurt anyone. Those are the reasons I'd rather mind travel. Music, science and reading are the only things that cause my mind to stop traveling.

Bush wins the election and I'm angry along with many others. Dukakis seemed to be a better candidate but I'm just a kid so maybe the adults know something about Bush that we don't know. He still looks sneaky with a crooked smile just like Mrs. Jasper's.

Anger eventually gets me banned from class instruction altogether. Instead of going to class I have to do all my work in the office of the principal Mr. Simmons. He's tall, slim, very dark, and stern in the face and he wears very nice suits. They have to actually take a desk down to the main office for me and I sit in a room where teachers copy and laminate papers which is a major distraction.

Not able to concentrate the noises and the fumes are major distracts me. Whenever a teacher comes into the room I flinch. Their presence takes me out of my thoughts because I'm on standby. Just in case somebody tries to hit or touch me, my right arm is on guard and sometimes I bend my knees to kneel from blows that don't exist. My mind and body are separate at times. I live and travel in my mind. Teachers try to force instruction but I play out too many scenarios in my head. There's always a lot to think about.

"Science, can't think about that. I have therapy today. Who's gonna see me in the embarrassing government car? What page was I on? When am I going to stop wearing training bras and get some titties? How are they gonna touch me when I get home? Does Daddy see what's happening to me from heaven? Are the dishes clean? Oh but here's my math and this long division is. Stop, pause. Cause the boys in the hood are always hard, you come talkin that trash we'll pull your card. Shake what ya Mama gave ya! I want a Jherie curl."

Looking at the clock I count down to lunch for an official break. Three more hours and I'm out of this dungeon with the loud machines, no walls and stinky toner. I call my space down with Mr. Simmons the dungeon. For the rest of the year this is where I have to learn.

Chapter 31

My days are far and few at Whythe and it's time to graduate from fifth. Somehow I manage to pass my grade and participate in the passing on ceremony. Everyone is told to wear white.

Wanting to design and sew my own graduation dress by hand I'm forced to wear a white pheasant looking dress that resembles something Laura Ingalls would wear as she runs through the fields hollering for her Pa.

Aside from my seat in the school's spelling bee and attending that science program at Hampton University for gifted students in the second grade, fifth grade graduation is a major accomplishment.

Frizzy curls and all here I am about to walk across the stage to accept my certificate which to me leads to the gateway of middle school. Anxiety sets in as I start to sweat profusely. Being shy, I've always been afraid of crowds but I can't be afraid today. I'm saying goodbye to the hallways and goodbye to the dungeon.

Mama is probably sitting in the audience waiting to watch me, her child who shares her exact same name. As I walk across the stage everything is still as I scan the sea of proud onlookers. Looking for the woman with the wild hair, bright makeup, high cheekbones and stunning smile, I see she's not here. The most important day of my life and Mama is not here.

After the ceremony everyone gathers for refreshments in the library. Goodbye to the place I gradually graduated from Puff the Magic Dragon to Judy Blume books and then on to Langston Hughes. In between I developed a fascination for World Records and Ripley's Believe It or Not.

Proud parents are everywhere and here I am looking for my caretakers. Finding them I'm in complete embarrassment. Mrs. Jasper looks fine as long as she doesn't holler and reveal the gray tooth, and the gap which means she probably should have lockjaw for a lifetime or at least while I'm around. Smiles should only be reserved for the home. What goes on behind closed doors should stay behind closed doors. Her husband is the sight of the day wearing plaid pants. It's now 1989 and colored Levis are in style. I'm glad this is my last day at this school and I hope most of my classmates will forget the fashion disaster over the summer break. If embarrassment could kill I'd be pushing up daisies right about now.

Lindsay Middle School is the next step in my journey after Wythe Elementary. Being put in an alternative class feels weird because there are only about eight to ten of us in class. My social worker and teachers says it's better for me. My teacher is now Mrs. Webber and she's beautiful and reminds me of Mama because she has big eyes like Diana Ross and high cheek bones. She has the longest fingernails and almost always wears high heels to school. I always asked her about her children and once again I imagine she is my Mama.

Therapy is ongoing and they say I have depression due to abuse and neglect. Honestly, the system doesn't care about me either. They cover up things better because they don't appear to be crazy and hide behind degrees. The whole system in my eyes is a joke. They're pretending to care as everyone gets a paycheck.

In middle school I become the queen of the hall.....not dance-hall.........the hall of the school. Pressing my back against walls I'm free from trying to learn. Watching my peers walk by I imagine what their lives are probably like for them at home.

My closest friends at school at this point are guys. Lamar, Sammy, and Doug are cool with me. Cracking jokes is what we do all the time. Lamar never gets sent out as much as the rest of us but he isn't as funny. Jokes drier than crackers, Lamar looks as if his parents care. He wears alligator shirts always starched, ironed and buttoned to the top. The rest of us dress ourselves and we pick our jokes better than we pick clothes. Whenever anyone joked on one of us there are repercussions from the whole crew.

Charles tried to crack on me one day and as the class laughed, he laughed and I smiled as I got up and beat him from the chalkboard, out the door and into the hallway. Stomping him with my shoe, my fellow jokesters gave me high fives because I left imprints of my Nike Cortez sole on the side of his face. Stomping as if I was smoldering a fire

I extinguished my anger and hurt for what was waiting for me at home.

At home I'm still my foster brother's secret toy. My period comes without warning so I'm a woman now. Learning about the birds and bees in fifth grade, I keep a book by Kotex I had been given in family life. The book comes in handy because I knew this day would come when Aunt Flo would come knocking. I overheard Mrs. Jasper talking to one of her friends once.

Her drunken friend looked me up and down and blurted, "Christine, that girl got a body on her. Has she started her monthly yet? Did you have the talk with her? I know the boys are after her."

Evenly tipsy Mrs. Jasper chimed, "Yeah, she done started. I ain't have to talk to her. That girl already read about it. She read everything she get her hands on, even encyclopedias. Yeah, she a little built that's why I keep her ass in the house."

Little does she know, the predators are in the same house as her, and even sleep in her bed.

They've really beat up my self-esteem which should be budding. My lips are their biggest target. Big lips, big legs, I'm dark, just ugly. My fashion sense is different too and my favorite outfit as of now is my tan pair of jeans, checkered tan and black blouse and tan cowgirl boots with tassels.

Getting off the Pentran city bus which doubles as our school bus, I clack my boots on the asphalt, into the grass and onto the cement. Having a Dolly Pardon moment I gallop because that's what cowgirls did. Wanting to hurry and throw my book bag down and ride my skates I continue to gallop.

"Damn, yo! She thick," a boy hollers.

Being used to attention my body attracts I continue to gallop. They want it.

Running up the stairs to the front porch I slam the door behind me and rush down the hallway to my bedroom and throw my book bag on my bed. BBD posters peer at me as I check my hair in the mirror. Frizzy strands everywhere and I don't care. Nobody cares about my mind, face or heart anyway. My legs are bigger than I desire and I hate them. Big legs...big lips...pure ugly.

No one is home but Moe and I try to hurry and grab my skates before he notices me but he catches me as I pull my skates from the hall closet. Yanking me and pulling me

down the hall through the library into the front room he
bends me over the couch backwards as he unzips his pants.

"Oh no," I think. "This is the day he's gonna do it. He's
gonna get in."

Trying to get in he kisses my neck as I clench my teeth
and close my eyes. I want to spit in his face and kill him
like I do in my dreams. Dreams of cutting his manhood off
and feeding it to the dogs or maybe I'll let it rot because if I
don't, I won't be the last.

My mind travels but I'm brought back to reality by Mrs.
Jasper's car pulling up. Moe runs with his pants around his
ankles and leaves me to get myself together. Dirty is how I
feel but I pray that he's never able to get in. The harder I
clench my teeth the more I'm able to resist him without
looking as if I'm putting up a fight.

Moe's not as bad and as slick as he thinks. I've never had sex but I've been "messed with" as they call it many times. Trying to make it seem as if nothing happen, I push the memory out of my head and run to get my skates. Here's to another secret. Moe almost got in but the car stopped him. Ahhhhh-hahhh! Moe didn't get what he wanted.

Chapter 32

God please help me out of this cell. I can't run that
suicide stuff now because there's nowhere else to go. How
do you get away from the people who are supposed to be
good? Somehow I gotta escape. Now I'm in the 8th grade
and I've been told I've had the most suspensions in the
whole school and I don't care. That's now my answer to
everything. I don't know and don't care.

Guts, I have plenty but the world doesn't know yet. As
Mr. Davis sits on the outdated furniture I look at his loafers
on the carpet. Different year, same loafers and still no
penny. How is this man supposed to manage my life?

Almost three years and his ass still hasn't come across a penny. Social services should fire him. I refuse to listen to a man who can't find a penny in three years.

"I want to leave, ready to move," I blurt.

"You ready to leave the Jaspers," Mr. Davis asked.

Still looking at the pea colored shag carpet I reply, "Yes, sir."

"Okay, let me get with my supervisor and we'll look for another home." He opens his folder and writes on his yellow legal pad. Now that's the mess that gets on my nerves. I know these people like clockwork. If I look at that paper it's probably scribbles.

"Since you know so much about my life Mr. Davis, where is your penny? Have you noticed you've been wearing penny loafers for almost three years, they need to

be shined and you have a church boy booty and your pants too tight," I want to say.

"Well, she wants to leave. I think she's tired here anyway," Mrs. Jasper says.

"Snagapuss, I have had enough of you acting concerned when you don't care. Let's tell Mr. Davis how you always tell me I'm not going to amount to anything. Let's tell him how you beat me. Let's tell him you tell me I will forever run from pillar to post." I almost blurt.

Tonight is the happiest night of my life. Looking out my window I look at the stars and tell them goodbye and thank them for sending messages to my brothers and sister. As always I wonder if they're looking up at the same star. Before I go to sleep I pray and wish for the day to see them again.

"Dear God, I pray for everyone. I pray that one day I won't hurt. I pray for Mitch and Kora. I pray for Mama and her mind and everyone. I ask for forgiveness for all the bad things I've done."

I go to bed reciting the Bible verse I've been reciting for years now. When I need strength, I will look to the hills...Sleep comes quick tonight and no one creeps into my room but I still wake up to make sure. I's almost free now...Color Purple...Celie…sleep. Goodnight.

Chapter 33

Today is the first day I'm not embarrassed to ride in the government car. Haven't smiled in a while and my heart feels free. Wind blows through my mind and my thoughts settle but my mind still travels

Pulling up to an apartment complex I look around because the only time I've lived in apartments was when I lived with Mama or her family. I didn't know foster parents live in apartments? Didn't know they were allowed to do that.

Mr. Davis and I leave my belongings in the car. There is laughter before we get to the door and I have a good feeling about this place. Stepping inside we're greeted by a beautiful, round, light skin woman. Stepping back she studies me as I study her.

Mr. Davis begins telling her a little about me but he doesn't know me. He doesn't know that I make clothes for the dolls I'm no longer able to play with because I'm 15. He doesn't know I still want to be a cheerleader, I want to learn a foreign language, I want to visit Paris and I want to learn to play the piano.

I smile and something tells me I'll learn many things at this home. Introductions are made as I meet her children, my new foster siblings. Her oldest son Darryl is lanky and is wearing a ball cap turned to the side. Not wanting to look at him because I don't want him to start liking me like my other foster brothers, I wave. Next is her oldest daughter Tasha. She's beautiful, has brown skin and is about my height but slim. We go to the same school and I had dreamed that I was her sister because I liked the way she dresses. Not only that, she's popular and wears makeup unlike me. I'd been prohibited from wearing nail polish at the Jasper's. There is another girl named Summer and she's pretty too and has the prettiest dark skin I've ever seen.

My new family is so beautiful. Usually there's an ugly one in the family but I haven't seen one yet. Everyone smiles at me and talks which is unusual to me. Happiness only finds me when I'm in my room or outside.

There is another foster child in the home and he looks like a piece of work. His name is Ray. At just three or four he looks to be a busybody. He has a toothy grin that makes me smile and honestly he resembled a little Too Short.

I like Too Short and I think I'm the only female amongst my friends who does. It doesn't matter because I love 2 Live Crew as well. Luther Campbell keeps it real but I was told "young ladies" don't listen to such filth. What happened to freedom of speech they preach about in school? I guess it pertains to which subject matter is being referred to. Listen to them in private is what I do. Tapes are hidden everywhere in my belongings so I can pop my coochie in the mirror and break it down to Me So Horny. I listen to the words sometimes but the Miami and Cali music have the beats my body craves for.

After the introductions I'm led up the stairs to where we're to sleep. The girls have twin beds in their room with a matching study. All their furniture is white and they have pretty pictures over their beds with little girls praying.

"How cute, I think. *"They some sweet little girls.....well I aint so sweet. I mean I am but I like Eazy E and I like to Pop My Coochie."*

They help me put my things into the closet and I pull out my framed 8x10 pictures. Thinking they are pictures of me they take one look and burst out in laughter.

"What" I ask.

The older sister chuckles, "This girl has pictures of Kwame in picture frames."

Not budging I reply, "Yep, Kwame is my boyfriend. Don't you like his polka dots and think he cute? I got his tape if you want to listen and I know all the words to every song."

We all laugh together and I can tell I'll grow to love this family. It's been a long time since people actually really took interest in me.

My new sisters have many questions for me and they make me feel comfortable. Opening up I'm no longer afraid because I know Mrs. Jasper can't beat me.

Sitting in a circle we talk and laugh until things begin to get serious.

"How was your last home," Tasha asks. Her eyes grow big as golf balls as she waits for an answer.

For the first time in almost three years the secrets are creeping out. Speaking of my former foster father feels creepy but I tell myself I'm free and no one can hurt me now.

"You need to tell my Mama. You can call her Ma because you live here and you're family now," says my new big sister.

Never have I called another woman Ma but it feels nice rolling off my tongue. Mrs. Waters did exactly as she's supposed to and told Mr. Davis even though I begged her not to. I think by law she's supposed to tell but Mr. Davis never said anything else to me about it. He didn't ask and I didn't tell. I don't tell him anything. All he does is enough to get a paycheck to keep driving that government car. No better than foster parents. Everyone is stupid if you ask me they tell me to act smart. If I follow their lead I'd be dumber than dumb. It's not that I'm dumb it's just my mind travels and most of the time I don't want to be here in this world because I don't fit in.

Chapter 34

Wanting to be a 'round 'da way girl I do my fair share of standing at bus stops sucking on lollipops. The bus stop is one of the neighborhood hangout spots. We also hang out in laundry mats, in the front of Getty Mart and the basketball court of Langley Square.

At the bus stop we watch people walk to Burger King and K-Mart and we shoo the city bus away whenever it stops for us to board. We act as if the bus stop belongs to us and not the city. Standing there makes me feel like a "round da way girl." Having my fake gold bamboo earrings makes me feel more like one and I'm beginning to really fit in.

As Tasha and I walk from Getty Mart we step into the kitchen and she says something to Ma. Not fully

understanding what's going on Ma is saying that we have
to catch the bus to the clinic the next day.

"Whats going on," I wonder. *I don't have to go to the
clinic. I heard you go there when you have VD or
something. Nothing is wrong with me and I'm used to Mr.
Davis or Snagapuss taking me to my appointments."*

"Janera, tomorrow you and Tasha have to take the bus
down to the clinic on Victoria Blvd."

Knowing that I shouldn't question adults I feel comfortable
with Ma but I want to know her reasoning.

"But why," I ask.

"Tasha going to get a pregnancy test or get on some pills
if she ain't. You going to get on the pill."

"But I'm not having sex. I don't want to have sex,"
anger fills me and I want to hit something to get her to

understand but I just run upstairs. Sliding down against the metal sliding closet door I flop on the carpet as if I'm a fish that's just jumped out of water.

"I don't want to have sex and don't want no pill. She think I'm going to get pregnant but how can I get pregnant if I ain't doing nothing? I'm not fast but I like boys and I actually just like the attention they give me that's all. I like the way they listen to me. One day I will have sex but I keep thinking about what Moe, Lewis, Mr. Jasper, the TV repairman, my cousin and another foster brother did to me. They wanted my body but they couldn't take it because I prayed to stay a virgin until marriage. I want to have some good left for my husband even though I have been touched a lot. I'm not all the way damaged goods like Celie was when Mister got her in the movie The Color Purple."

Sitting at the same bus stop that allows me to feel like a 'round da way girl' makes me feel dirty. While waiting for the bus Tasha tries to talk to me but my mind travels.

"I don't need protection, don't need no pills and I don't need to go to no clinic. People gonna see me and think I got VD."

The white, yellow and blue PenTran bus is coming to a halt and I can hear the wetness of the asphalt meet the rubber of the tires on the bus. Once the door opens, people exit from both the front and rear doors. We pay our fare and slide onto the blue seats. Tasha continues to talk but I prefer to take my friend silence along for our journey to the clinic. Inside the clinic it reminds me of the clinic downtown Newport News Mama used to take me to a long time ago.

Terrified I ask Tasha so many questions she decides it's best if she escorts me for my examination.

"I'm scared," I spit.

"You ain't got nothing to be scared of," she sits as if we're in church, like everything is normal.

"But I ain't never had anything inside me. I mean they tried but nothing ever got in. It's gonna hurt, I know it is."

My name is called and Tasha walks with me. Zoning out the nurse, I take the papers, sign more papers and just stare at the pictures on the wall. Posters look like the diagrams in my book I still have from my fifth grade family life class. It's been three years but at the age of 15 I am not ready for this. My mind isn't ready and I still want to be digging in the trash at the Jasper's hoping to find the Barbie's they say I'm too big to play with. I want to play with my Barbie's forever but instead here I am at the clinic.

Pulling myself together after what I learned beforehand was a pelvic exam, I slip back into my clothes and pick up my purse and stuff my clinic papers inside. Still carrying the picture of Daddy I make sure I don't rip the one thing that's tangible proof that he lived. Social Services acts like he never existed because they never took the time to see what a great man he was. I bet Daddy wouldn't send me to catch the bus to a clinic.

Tasha has been checked too but she has something different because she's been tested to see if she's pregnant. Her test came back positive and she cries a little but I don't understand why she isn't going off. She's calm and acts very mature about the situation. I would run far away and hide from everyone forever.

Retrieving my birth control pills from the lady behind the counter, I listen as she gives me instructions along with a brown bag of condoms. She hands me my boarding pass to have sex. Tasha has to return for another appointment. I'm out once again disconnected from everyone and I'm chillin' in my head watching the clock until it's time to get on the bus to go home.

"This lady is whack too. Nobody knows me. I'm not ready to have sex and they're going to see. I don't need these condoms. I'm a good girl even if bad things happened to me. Mrs. Jasper said girls get ruined by the time they grown when they have sex early. Don't want to use up my good stuff as a child because I still kinda want my Barbie's.

Back in school I let my friends know I have more freedom. Mrs. Waters tells me how important it is that I get an education because she doesn't have one but it looks like she's living good to not have one. Everyone has nice clothes, nice furniture, and cable TV. Life looks good for her and she has better furniture than the Jasper's and she even told me she went to the Bahamas. She's doing well without an education. Maybe she need to take Mr. Davis shopping and tell him he went to the wrong school because they didn't teach him much of nothing except how to get that paper to allow him to be a social worker. A woman with no education is doing better than the guy who went to school for years. Life is funny sometimes.

My new home brings new-found freedom. I'm now allowed to wear makeup and I have free range of my neighborhood aka hood. One of my new privileges is being allowed to have a boyfriend...not that I really want one but I do think a few guys are cute.

Tasha shows me how to wear my makeup. Initially, I only line my big brown eyes with black eyeliner and I smack color on my full lips with lipstick. My new big sister fixes my hair for me. I look up to her and she is everything I want to be. We hang pretty tight and stay up night telling stories and talking about boys.

Guys begin to take interest in me even though I still fought a bit in school. I don't like boys my age because they know me from school. Older cats don't go to school with me and can't find out I dance and laugh in the hallways of school. One after another I date and admire guys as I try to go after the bad boys.

No longer being the new kid on the block there's a newer kid named Larry. He's kinda cute with pimples and brown skin. His Mama takes care of him by herself and he wears nice clothes. Larry's preppy and tries to be street. He's my age and has expressed an interest in me. I don't like him like that because he's my age and is a little too reserved.

As I sit in the living room watching Brand Nubian's *Slow Down*, I'm interrupted by Darryl, one of my foster siblings. "Janeraaaaa. Somebody wants you at the door and it's a boy. Janera got a boyfriend, Janera got a boyfriend."

"Shut up," I shoot him an evil eye and laugh.

Getting up from the couch I wonder who could be at the door. A few guys like me but I know exactly what they want. Darryl left my visitor to stand outside so as I swing the door open there stands a shy Larry. "Can you come outside?"

Chewing my gum as if I'm a horse chewing straw, "Naw, I'm in here watching Yo! MTV Raps. You can come in if you want."

Opening the door he stepped in as he extends his hand giving me a pretty foil bag. Opening it I see he's given me some bath fizzies and chocolates. So this cat listens to me when we talked briefly the other day. Nice gestures but I'm not impressed at all. He probably took all this from his mother. Minding my manners I thank him politely.

"Thank you, you shouldn't have." If he's thinking I'll be his girlfriend he needs to think again. I like older guys point blank. His mom probably won't allow him to hang out with me along the Langley Square fence.

I ask him to sit and make himself comfortable on the blue floral couch. We watch Chi Ali's *Age Aint Nothing But a Number*, but I hope he doesn't think it's true in his case. We'll stay friends for eternity. Not wanting him to talk, my eyes stay glued to the TV. He intercepts my mind from traveling.

"Sooooo." he yawns. What is he gonna try to say now. Don't try it because I'm not impressed. Blowing bubbles and popping them with my straight teeth I wait. Swallowing my gum, I tell myself that I'm not acting lady like. Straightening my posture I try to get the watermelon wad down my throat. He now has my attention but only as

a friend.

"You think maybe you and I can go to the movies," he

asks but I refuse to let him finish.

"Don't like movies. Let's go outside." I stand and he

followed. I loved when people do as I say. For so long

people had power over me and I'm taking mine back.

Outside I'm free to talk because I know Darryl had been

listening. He joked me about boys all the time.

With my fresh Patrick Ewing's sneakers and tight jeans

I make him look at my full lips.

"Listen to me. You're nice and all but you're not my

type. You're my age and I like older guys. We can hang

out and study but that's it."

He didn't say anything. Larry just walked away with silence realizing that age is more than a number and it means a lot to me.

Chapter 35

Nobody can feel my love. I don't know if people really love. Can I still love? I know one thing, I'm gonna hold on to my virginity. I've lost clothes and a bunch of pictures but I still hold on to my sanity.

Life with my new family isn't so bad. In the apartment complex there's a pool. I have a new bathing suit that's black with 3 gold bows holding it together at the sides. The guys think I'm cute in it but I wish they wouldn't look at me but hey, boys gonna be boys. As long as they don't touch me let them look. They call me the "Pool Queen" and I like it...kinda. I mean I fell in love with the pool because the water makes me feel good. First time ever anyone referred to me as a Queen. They line up at the fence and yell for me to get out the water. They don't know I stay in the pool all day....partly because I love the water and partly because I don't want them looking at my butt. See I know what they want, I got what they want and I ain't giving it up because I'm holding on to my love and virginity. I been staying in the damn pool so much I'm sunburned......red, scaly, but I'm happy. I skip and gallop home sometimes from the pool. I'm the Pool Queen and I can laugh freely. I don't have to fight in this home because things are different.

Being that I've been in therapy for nine years now, nothing has changed in my opinion. I go to them so they can get paid. They give me advice...yadda, yadda, yadda. Everyone gets paid. Same stuff different year. They don't even tell me anything's wrong with me but say I have to keep going because of trauma.

They don't really know about my pain because I ain't telling them. I mean there's enough there for them to see but I think everyone is stupid and those degrees sometimes make them blind. I can do my work but I can't concentrate and I kinda gave up when my Daddy died fighting for custody because I was that close to happiness but God said he needed him more than I did. I know it's not right to question God so I gotta keep living and doing time in these foster homes. This one ain't so bad but these voices with me tell me Daddy alright and I'm gonna be too. I'm

I listen to my music everyday. I'm hooked on a lot of people and Kwame is still my boyfriend. I still have all the pictures I saved from Word Up magazine in 8x10 frames. I dumped Al B. Sure because light skin went out of style when I met Kwame. See, I'm not color struck like my real Mama. She's different and I'm nothing like her at least not in that way. I'm also hooked on Tony Terry and Will Downing.

There's a guy who's kinda shy and goofy, tall and light skin. His name is Calvin and he notices more than my body and we spend plenty of time together talking about life. As I start spending time at his house he makes me sing that Color me Badd song, *I wanna sex you up*.

My therapy sessions go smoothly and my grades are finally coming up. Everyone thinks my new relationship has calmed me down.

We go through the cow pasture, ducked under wooden gates, creep through a fence. He doesn't care if I gallop, I'm his and he's mine. Today is the day that I want Calvin to make me a woman. Betty Wright is singing in my head. Going into the apartment in Sinclair Gardens we sneak upstairs.

A lot of heat is ignited and there's fire everywhere. The radio is helping with the mood. Nope, I can't wait another minute. Hi-Five is jamming and we're now on the bed and all talking has ceased.

We both looked down. .....Oh no....my period. SHIT!!!!!

Something told me it wasn't time and not with him.

"It's ok baby," he whispers.

Wanting to give him something he can feel to let him know my love is real; I accept that Mother Nature knows best. Maybe it's a sign.

Shielding me and covering me we sneak back to Mercury Square. Calvin kisses me and I slip into the door quietly and tiptoed up the stairs to shower.

I know what's gonna happen will happen, but this ain't the day that anyone will make me a woman.

Chapter 36

Imagining I'm standing on the cliff like Paula Abdul in her video *Rush, Rush...... Here there I stand... Hurry, hurry lover come to me.*

My boyfriend and I begin to drift apart. Walking through the parking lot I seen him three buildings down walking away from one of my schoolmates apartments. Heart hurt a little. Thinking he was the one I took my natural disaster with Ant Flo as a sign but I continue to entertain him. We still hang out, walk and talk all the time.

I loved staying out of the house because there are too many people in the apartment most of the time. Everywhere I turn there's someone and I have no peace to read or listen to music by myself.

My summer love affair of 1991 has been disrupted by a bullet. A bullet tore Calvin and I apart. There's been a murder in our apartment complex. I liked being away from the touches but this is another world I'm not used to. I basically grew up over night.

I wasn't allowed to wear nail polish and now I stand with my mask on. Showing them I'm one of them. I want to look like some of the girls in the videos kinda but I want to show people I'm no dummy. My mind goes to the Elephant Man; I am not an animal, I am a human. They're gonna see that Mama and I are alike in some ways but I'm different because I want to break this cycle they say I'm in.

The crime causes us to move into a very small house on Woodland Rd. I loved was the fact I'll be going to a different school. Hampton High has ghosts which are the same ghosts that roam the hallways of C. Alton Lindsey Middle School. The ghosts are my friends, the people I fight, the people who can't figure me out as they wonder why I act the way I do.

I crack jokes because I don't want to face reality because I'm still trying to store shit on a floppy disk. Time is moving and it's not stopping for me or anyone else. Didn't have time to heal because they aren't telling anything's wrong with me. All they keep slapping me with is depression. Their words were depressing and acting out is my way of releasing the anger.

Grabbing words from music because I haven't written anything since I was ten and Mama locked us in the rooms away from everyone. Even though Mama had padlocked us in rooms I had peace. Playing with the words in my head makes sense to me in this crazy world. They never believed me when I told them angels visit me. They made it seem like one was bad and one was evil but they're not. They're both good and they've been with me since

Daddy left. The angels and I know better. They told me they'll always be with me and told me I'm going to have to go through more things but they'll be with me every step of the way. We're about to show them this ain't nothing like crazy.

Summer of 1991 I'm enrolled in Phoebus High School. Entering the school I take a breath of the fresh air. New school, new start and I'm now free to be me. They talked about my new school being first constructed to be a mall in 1975. Amazed that the place was erected the same year I presented myself to this earthly plane we connected. This is my school and I like the colors because they rep blue and gold. Blue is Mama's favorite color.....something else to send to the stars to tell her through messages. I've been sending messages to the stars many nights and I talk to them. It's been my secret. The sun, the moon and the stars are my friends and they give me a closer connection to God. Nobody can take that away from me. I give God all my secrets but somehow the angels know because they're always reassuring me that everything will be ok and they tell me to calm down. .

Going to my new school I meet new friends and find that it isn't hard as I thought it'd be. No one knows me and I don't know them. I elect to learn a foreign language which is a dream come true. I still gotta hide my love for Greek mythology. Can't tell let all my secrets out because when I do sometimes I get labeled white, weird or trying to be something I'm not.

People talk like this school bad but it's not to me. This is a clean start. I love looking at the blue and yellow phantom. So much power is here and the eyes of the phantom tell me so much.

"Hey Janera. I have someone I want you to meet." Following Tammy, my short and stubby new friend, I feel as though something was up.

"Who is it? Do I know this person?" She keeps me in suspense.

Pushing through the double doors we go down the hall and turn right. Classes are divided by partitions so it's easy to look over them and see desks but everyone is busy changing classes.

Coming closer to our destination she mumbles under her breath. "You and this girl were dating Calvin at the same time."

Surprisingly I'm face to face with a brown skin girl about my height, maybe an inch shorter. She has a modified

Halle Berry haircut. She has brown hair to match her friendly brown eyes. She's wearing a green long sleeved green tunic, a brown skirt and matching green opaque tights. I could tell she likes to shop at The Limited.

Tammy moves to the side as if she's a matador. I guess that was my cue to act a fool and rage like a bull.

"Janera this is Alicia. Alicia, meet Janera."

We stand in silence just looking at one another.

Breaking the ice I sighed, "So, you gotta use the bathroom? I need to powder my nose."

Alicia smiles and agrees. We walk in unison clutching our books, turning our backs to Tammy forgetting she even exists. She thought she'd see a fight but we outsmarted her. I'm smart enough to gain control by powdering my nose.

Chapter 37

So my foster mom and social worker seem to think that putting me on medication will help.

My grades have improved and my attitude is a little better but it has nothing to do with those little red pills I hide and tell them I forget to take.

I have people who are showing a genuine interest in me with no expectations. Talking to my boyfriend seems to help a lot and I've formed a bond with my foster mom's brother. I feel comfortable calling him Uncle Randy.

Just like the others I'm apprehensive around him at first making sure he doesn't want anything in return. Uncle Randy talks to me...I mean really talks to me. He asks me about my future, my grades and it's not because he's getting paid to do it either.

Talking to Uncle Randy gives me relief. He understands my uniqueness and tells me that I'm just fine. I love it when he comes to visit. He's a big, tall brown skinned man with curly hair...except not on top. He's real shiny at the top. His head matches his belly... round.

I've also formed a bond with my foster grandmother who I easily call Grandma. Never called anyone else Grandma besides my real Grandma. Since I left the Jasper's I still long for my church and my new Grandma takes me to gospel signings and she really loves the Sunset Travelers. For some reason I love hanging with older people anyway although my foster sisters don't quite understand. Older people teach me so much and the fried chicken after the singings usually come from Chic A Sea. It's a little greasy but so good.

Hanging with Grandma gives me my quiet time. It's not so quiet at my new home because there's always someone there and I guess I'm so used to being alone

reading, sewing, painting and anything else that comes to

my mind. They just don't understand that the things I do

help me to escape the world that has caused me so much

pain.

Grandma has a home in York County and I love it

out there. My foster sisters say there's nothing to do out

there but sometimes that's what I like to do; absolutely

nothing. Spending time outside lying in the grass is what I

do. These are the things that make people say I'm

different. I like doing what other girls my age do but they

expect me to fall right into place when I've been out of

place for so long.

Alongside having to watch out for my siblings, the

beatings, the touching and being isolated...I AM different.

Knowing that when I'm in my world there's no hurt. *Little*

Women by Louisa May Alcott, *I Know Why The Caged*

Bird Sings by Maya Angelou, the many years of reading about Fudge and his brother Peter given to me by Judy Blume causes no hurt. Sewing, listening to music, doing macramé, learning about plants, feeding the fish are all peaceful. Now I'm hooked on cross-stitch but here at my new home I don't do those things because I don't have the money to buy supplies. I'd been caged for so long and now here I am roaming free like the cattle in the cow pasture. I guess I must find my way and hang on to my pieces of peace any way I can.

Chapter 38

I pray everyday and ask God to just let me get to 18 so I can be free from this prison. I dream of the day I will be free. I'm gonna run through the field like Celie ran to her family. I don't even care if there's not a family to run to, freedom is what I want.

Uncle Randy sings on the church choir, loves God and can cook. He wasn't too keen in school and dropped out. That's what he told me. He tells me he's a self-made man. I had to look that one up because I really didn't know what it meant. He's made a good life for himself and his family. Self-made is definitely good because he's doing OK.

"Uncle Randy I've seen some shoes I want. Do you think you can get them for me?"

Looking me in my eyes as he always does when he talk he put his big hands together.

"Some shoes."

"Yes sir." I nod.

"So, you just want me to buy you some shoes?"

"Yes, sir. They're in Bakers. I been looking at them for a couple of weeks."

Now leaning in the chair he looked up at the ceiling and chewed on the toothpick he had in his mouth.

Knowing Uncle Randy he's about to tell me something I should know.

"Let me tell you something. In life, nothing is just given to you. You have to earn things. No one gives me anything. So what I want you to do is pull those grades up and then we'll talk about those shoes."

I knew he was serious and Uncle Randy always kept his word but I want those shoes.

I have an interesting teacher in a class that's supposed to help me study for all my other courses. My teachers name is Mrs. Withers. She's a white woman in her 40's maybe and I love the way she dresses. She wears bohemian skirts, Birkenstock sandals, and jewelry made of copper and beautiful crystals. While giving us rundown of the class expectations I notice she's a bit different.

She introduces us to affirmations and explains that words have power and we could do whatever we want if we simply believe. At first I think she's a quack. Mrs. Withers tells us that we should write down what we want to accomplish and speak it repetitively on a daily basis. She says we should practice at home in the mirror.

Now everyone in the house is really gonna think I'm nuts talking to myself in the mirror but anything is worth a try. Besides, I want those shoes.

Chapter 39

I now begin my affirmations. Right now I want those shoes so I gotta bring my grades up. I'm 15 and will soon be 16 in the 9th grade. I've never repeated a grade but did start school late because Mama didn't send me when I needed to go because I was in the closet but people don't see that today. All they see is a girl who's not in the right grade.

I will make honor roll.

I will bring my grades up.

I will make honor roll.

I will bring my grades up.

Everyday that's what I chant in the mirror before I prepare to get ready for school.

Working hard is what I do and I stayed in my books every chance I could get. My favorite subjects are English and Latin and I continue to hide my love for writing because I don't want to be made fun of.

I even signed up for some extra curricular activities and joined the SCA (Student Council Association).

By the time report cards come out I was hope to see more than the flags (F's) I had last year. I am amazed when I found out I've made the honor roll. Mrs. Wither's method works. I listen to every word she says from now on. That lady knows her stuff.

My social worker is going to be amazed that the affirmations, not those little pills, worked like a charm.

Chapter 40

Hopefully I'm showing everyone that I'm nothing like my mother. Some people try to tell me I'm going to be just like her but they don't know the things I know about her. They don't know her secrets and they don't know her qualities. All they know is what is on paper which is mostly bad. I know better and I will be nothing like her. The only thing she and I have in common is DNA.

At my new school I'm not looked at as the bad kid, the kid who's sent out into the hallway. I'm not the class clown anymore. The guys are paying me a lot of attention.....good attention. Seems like yesterday I was restricted from doing anything, getting beat, felt on, kissed, lived as the black Cinderella and now I'm free to do a lot, don't have to clean as much, no unwanted touches or kisses and I now can live as a teenager. I've escaped from the dungeon and I'm loving my new life.

I have a new boyfriend and I reminisce about the day our eyes and hearts began to connect.

My foster sister and I were walking to 7-11 and out of nowhere came a red car blaring reggae music.

Scrrrr.......screaching tires as the Chevrolet Cavalier almost hits the light pole in front of us.

Giggling, Tasha and I thought that we had seen the car before going up and down the street.

Interrupting our late afternoon walk to the store was not one but two guys. They had raced to the scene as if they were Batman and Robin.

Batman, or the dark skinned stocky one jumped out so quick and sat on the hood of the car. We continued to watch as Robin, the slim brown skinned brother got out and leaned on the passenger side.

Tasha and I looked at one another and burst in laughter. We were speechless.

"Yo, come here. What's your name," belted the one on the hood of the car.

Looking around I shrugged my shoulders. "Who, me?" I asked.

"Yeah, you", he replied.

"You want to talk to me so you need to come over here." I was beginning to like the game we were playing. I forgot that there were two bystanders. My sister and skinny guy AKA Robin were still nearby. Turning to look for my sister I realized that she was talking to Robin, blushing just as hard.

Stocky guy walked over to me. *Hmmmm.......he's a cutie. Deep chocolate complexion, cute mole on his face and broad shoulders. He probably plays football.*

Walking over to me so confidently he had a distinct walk that said, 'don't mess with me'.

"I like that. He's probably a protector."

"So are you going to tell me your name or not? You look nice."

I could tell that he was from up north by the accent. Brooklyn was my guess.

"My name is Janera."

"Nice to meet you Janera, I been watching you and I like what I see. My name is Danny."

Our eyes met and something clicked. An inferno in our souls ignited. Stepping back I interrupted the awkwardness of our meeting.

"Ummmm...We have to get to the store to pick up something for our Mama and she'll be mad if we don't hurry back." I hoped he believed my white lie.

"So can I come see you sometimes and take you out," he asked.

Trying to keep my composure I didn't want him to know how much I wanted to say yes, yes and yes again I simply replied, "I have to ask my Mama."

"Why don't I ask her myself," he blurted.

Now my palms are sweaty, heart is racing and I'm super nervous.

Looking at the traffic zooming by I stared at the sky to take my eyes off him.

"Well, we're having a party for my nephew today. You can come over. There will be others stopping by so I guess it'll be cool."

"Why don't you write down your address and I'll be by. I really want to see you. You have a boyfriend?"

I shook my head and giggled.

"You are going to be my girl. You know that right?"

"Whatever you say." Looking over at my sister I started to walk away. "Well, it was nice meeting you but we have to go. Come on Tasha. We need to get back to the house and finish decorating for the party."

We said our goodbyes and the little red car sped off and that was the beginning of real love.

Chapter 41

Back at home everyone is excited about the party. My mind was still on other things but mostly Danny. I really don't think he'll show up.

As usual, there are many people in the house and Tasha is preparing little Alex for his party.

A car has pulled up with loud music. Peeping out the blinds I see Danny and the butterflies set in. He kept his word which makes me smile. Running up the stairs to the bathroom I fix my hair and freshen up my lipstick. As I run down the stairs I notice someone has let him in and our eyes meet. He has a rose in his hand.

Standing face-to-face he extends the rose. "This is for you."

My first flower from a guy, this is sweet.

I take my new friend by the hand. "Come on. Let me introduce you to Mama. Don't be scared, she's going to look at you mean but she means no harm."

Leaving the living room, we walk through the dining room to my foster mother's bedroom where she's sitting.

"Ma this is Danny."

Mama looks him up and down but I'm used to this now. She does it every time she has serious questions.

"So, you want to date my daughter, huh," she asks.

"Yes, ma'am."

Turning to me Mama said, "Janera, let us talk in private. I have a few questions to ask this fellow."

"Yes, ma'am," I reply.

In the living room my sisters sit. There's now a new sister living in the house. She's cool and is also a foster child. Her name is Sharice and she's older than me by nine months. She and Tasha have birthdays days apart so that means there are three of us girls in the house the same age. How fortunate, I'm ready for an episode of Clash of the Teenagers.

Friends come and go as we prepare for the day's festivities. Someone's outside starting up the grill. Cookouts are my favorite because they remind me of my Aunt Mattie and she's my connection to my family on my mother's side.

"Do you think Mama will let me date him?" I just want to know what Tasha thinks.

"She probably will but I don't know."

Twenty minutes later the door to Mama's bedroom opens and out walks Mama and Danny. He has a smile on his face so I know that's a good sign.

August 1, Danny and I begin to really get to know one another. He says he doesn't want to sleep with me and that's a relief but I know that eventually he'll probably want more than conversation but hopefully he understands that right now I'm not ready. I really want to wait until marriage. In my 16 years I've seen a lot from men and I only want to share my body with my husband. It'll be nice to be special to someone at some point. Dating Danny is blowing my mind because he's a total gentleman and is smart. He attends Norfolk State University and is majoring in political science. Discovering my love for reading he tells me that I should be reading more thought provoking material to challenge my mind. He introduces me to writings of the great Elijah Muhammad and tells me of trailblazers like Marcus Garvey. He tries to explain mental slavery to me and tells me of corruption but to me politics is corruption so his formal education is a joke somewhat. Honestly, at this point in my life I feel that corruption is everywhere.

Having had disclosed the fact that I was still a virgin was a big mistake. I didn't see why it's such a big deal because I've chosen to save myself. I have other things to concentrate on. My cousin Jewel who I talk to all the time has a tumor on her brain, I still wonder about the whereabouts of my siblings and my mother and I have to start planning for what's to come after I leave foster care because I know it will be me against the world.

Feeling as though I'm a black sheep the heat is on.

"Janera, when you trying to give up the draws girl. What you got on, a chastity belt," screams Darryl.

The whole house bursts out in laughter but deep down I don't like being the center of jokes especially when they're personal. The jokes aren't limited to my lack of sexual activity they also spread to my bloodline.

"Yeah, we know about your Mama. We hear she's a few sandwiches short of a picnic basket. She's craaaaaaazy." Darryl's joke cuts very deep because I don't understand Mama and neither does he.

Those are the jokes I can't pull myself to laugh at. They pierce my heart because even though Mama didn't do right by me, she's still Mama. Those jokes make me hot under the chin as tears well in my eyes. They make me drift and as usual I go in the bathroom to release the flow of tears.

Closing my eyes I pray. Dear God I didn't ask to be here. I didn't ask for her to be my Mama but I love her. Why do I still love her but I hurt? Why didn't Mama protect me the way I protect her sometimes. God, please help me.

Chapter 42

Danny and I are hanging pretty tight while I try to hang on to my grades. Instead of trying to find a quiet place to read or study every now and then, I'm with him. During the beginning of the schoolyear it was OK because it was easier but I'm worried that I'll have to cram for exams. My foster mother suggests I call my relationship off but I don't think I want to do that. Besides, I'm in love.

Rocking to the beat of Mary J. Blige's Real Love, Danny and I fall deeper and deeper. He even dedicated that song to me. That song was written for us and we claimed it wholeheartedly. The album *What's the 411* is a lyrical storybook that I read and sing it every day. My mind travels with hooks, beats and the rhythm while my heart skips beats over and over.

"You know you're my Queen, right." Danny said out of nowhere.

Just looking at him I don't know what to say so he begins to explain as my eyes flicker question marks.

"You're my Queen and you should always be treated as such. I will never hurt you, disrespect you or lie to you. I feel bad that you had to grow up the way you did living in so many homes. I'm never going to let anyone harm you. You're the best and you deserve nothing but the best. Always remember that."

Not knowing what to say I'm shocked because guys have told me they love me, I'm pretty and I even had guys who said they didn't like me being in foster care but never have I had someone whose actions matched the words.

I'm used to people saying one thing but doing something else. I'm used to people leaving. I'm used to doing something to make people not like me. I'm used to keeping so much to myself but Danny says we're best friends and I've opened up to him. I didn't tell him everything though. I don't think he'd be able to understand it all because I don't understand half of it. He knows about the six guys who touched me from six to fifteen and I think that's why he tells me sex is no issue. I know he's lying. He's just trying to not hurt my feelings.

"Danny, thank you for being here for me. Thank you for listening but I know you're a little older and you may want to do things I can't do because I'm only 16. You're in college. Why do you want me? Why do you care? I know you'll leave one day."

"I'm never leaving. It's you and I. You have a strong mind and some people can't handle that and don't know why you fight. You're a fighter but you have to learn to fight smart. One day if not now, you'll understand and it and it will all make sense. You're greater than these people will ever know. I feel it. You're special, a gift and that's why you've survived so much. There's a purpose that we don't know right now but you have to stay strong and remember to never allow anyone inside your head. People will control you by your thoughts. Continue to think for yourself. You're different, cute, a little green, but nothing is wrong with that."

My smile breaks with the word green.

"Green? I'm green? What's that supposed to mean?"

"It just means you don't know the streets that well."

"I'm no dummy," I yell as I pull away from him.

Pulling me close he hushes me.

"Look, you're no dummy. You just lived a sheltered life. I know you're intelligent but book and street smart is different. Being green isn't so bad. Take it as a compliment but you don't have to worry about that because you got me."

His big fist pounds his heart and my smile is back.

"I'm a little different too. I think for myself and always will. We're both Scorpio's which means we're headstrong and different anyway. You're my Bonnie and I'm Clyde."

"Who are Bonnie and Clyde? I never read about them but I think I heard of them."

"They were a badass couple. They did a lot together and were loyal to one another. Clyde taught Bonnie to be tough."

"Sounds like a plan. Count me in"

"You know that I'm out in the streets sometime doing my thing; my hustle. You'll never see that. I promise you. I respect you and you've been through enough but you have to know there's a way you have to move out here on the streets. You have to be smooth. See, I don't look like I hustle. I go to school and then I have a job, outside of that my time is with you and when I'm not with you, you know what it is. Just know that I'm yours and my heart is with you at all times. Promise me that you trust me."

"I trust you."

We slap a hi-five and kiss as we crumple our lips and twist our faces trying to look mean to one another. Laughter fills the room and just like most nights I fall asleep on his chest instead of my textbooks.

Chapter 43

School is going well. I'm still motivated to do my best but I'm always thinking about whether I'll see Danny after school. During school Alicia and I meet up in the foreign language hall towards the end of the day because while I'm taking Latin she's taking German.

Rocking a pair of bell bottom Cross Colors jeans, a cool t-shirt and a pair of bohemian sandals it's evident that my confidence begins to rise. Alicia and I talk about everything but mostly the goings on in school, fashion and our boyfriends.

Alicia is wearing some trendy threads as well but her family buys all her gear which makes me wonder what that's like. My boyfriend does a lot for me even though I don't ask. He acts as if I'm his responsibility sometimes.

After school is out I board the city bus which doubles as our transportation to and from school.

On the bus I like to keep quiet because I don't want people to hear my business but my sister Tasha doesn't have any problem with it. I'm not really quiet but I'm used to keeping things to myself and I know that sometimes people can hear the smallest thing and get the wrong idea. Some of the things we talk about are not appropriate to be talked about publicly so I laugh off most of it or I render a whisper whenever I feel an answer is mandatory.

Soon I will be 17 and I still haven't gone all the way with my boyfriend. It makes me feel a little different and sometimes I think if I go ahead and have sex the jokes will stop. I'm going to have to see about that.

Danny and I are alone and finally I want to go all the way with him. I feel I have to prove that I'm not an outsider, uncool and I don't want to lose my relationship either.

"Come on, I'm ready," I snap.

Danny snaps away from the music we'd been listening to.

"Ready for what? What you talking about?"

Taking a gulp I stand stiff as a board, head high as if I'm about to jump from a cliff.

"I'm ready to have sex."

"Are you sure? It's no big deal to me and I want you to wait until you're ready."

"Didn't you hear me? I'm ready."

Danny is beginning to irritate me because now he's beginning to act green. Noticing he's still a bit apprehensive I start to undress and I leap over the cliff. Danny did as I asked in an almost demanding way. Just like that I threw away something I had cherished. At least I'm in control initially. It feels different because I'm used to being told what to do but this time I called the first shot.

Riding home I notice Danny isn't really saying anything to me and we're not laughing, kissing or cracking jokes over his loud music and aggressive New York driving skills.

Pulling up to the two story house as I'm barely making curfew on a school night he turns the car off. My nerves are a wreck and the confidence I had a couple hours ago is playing hide and go seek. My boyfriend turns to me and I close my eyes; maybe he's going to dump me.

"Are you alright," he asks.

"Yes, I'm fine. I'm just a little tired."

"I love you with all my heart, Janera. You're special."

"You still think I'm special?"

"Of course I do. Why wouldn't I? You were born special. Didn't you know that?"

"You're just trying to make me feel good."

"I don't have to try to do anything and I'm telling you the truth. Now gimme a kiss and have a good night. I'll pick you up after school tomorrow."

"No, I don't need you to pick me up. I'm going to ride the bus with my sisters."

"OK," he says as he gets out opening my door. Kissing me on my lips he asks, "I'm Clyde so who are you?"

"Bonnie is who I am."

"Damn right! That's us for eternity. Bonnie and Clyde and don't you forget it. We don't have to be like anyone but us. I love you, Bonnie."

"I love you Clyde."

Once inside the home I keep quiet, creep upstairs, shower and get ready for bed as I play out tomorrows conversation on the bus in my mind. I'm going to surprise them and they'll have no choice but to get off my back. I jumped over the cliff and into some grownup stuff. Now I'm like them, well almost.

Chapter 44

Thinking that since I'm on their side, one of them the jokes would end; they don't. The subject matter is now strictly based on Mama or just me being different. I'm not picked on or anything like that but when the daggers are thrown my heart catches them.

Danny had been taking me to see my cousin Jewel more often because her tumor has turned for the worse and she's not getting any better. The doctors said she now has cancer. The last time I was able to visit her she didn't look well, was unable to speak but I knew she understood my words. I tried to hold back my tears but I had never seen her like that before. She was unable to do anything for herself.

The next time I had gone to visit her as I got out of Danny's car, her mother, my Aunt Brenda stopped me.

"How dare you tell the family that Brent molested you? Take it back. That's a lie."

"Aunt Brenda it's not a lie. He did touch me and you walked in one day when he had me on his lap."

"You're a liar and I don't want you coming around here anymore. Jewel wouldn't like you saying such things about her brother."

"But Aunt Brenda, Jewel knows the truth. She just can't talk right now. Can I please see Jewel?" I raised my arms as if to ask why, I freeze.

"You will not see Jewel now get away from here."

I begin to run with tears in my eyes as Danny has heard and seen everything.

"Come here." Danny pulls me into his arms and wipes my tears. "You know the truth and God knows the truth and that's all that matters. Your Aunt probably doesn't want to acknowledge that her son has done those things. I don't think any mother would."

"But Danny, it's not about me and not about the things Brent did to me when I was younger. I just want to see Jewel. You know how she was the last time. She's not going to live long. I felt it. I know."

In Dickerson Court I begin to feel the same way I felt when Daddy died. Feeling as if I'm about to faint Danny grabs me tight, puts me in the car and we speed away making our way back to our familiar ground of Hampton.

Hurt by the events at my Aunt's place my hurt is deep. Even though I am still in therapy which I've been since 1981, I feel I can't really open up because no one understands my world. I've been through too much. I've only opened up mostly to Danny. He's better than therapy and doesn't get paid to deal with me. Kids like me are just dollar signs. We're money for the foster parents and I wonder how many would let me stay for free. We're money for the social workers because without us they wouldn't have a job. Basically anyone who has to sign anything with my name on it is getting paid. I feel that they don't care the way they should because they could never know my struggle. The books they studied in school don't tell of the stories I know, I've live the crap. I'm a 17 year old veteran of life and I'm ready to leave.

I feel out of place in my foster home at this point because I don't think like them. Why won't people allow others to think for themselves? I don't have the same interests and I get called hardheaded and headstrong. Yes, I am all of that because that makes me, me. I like what I like and I have a mind of my own.

Although I've lived in many homes and have been through a lot, I'm not used to this life of being around so many people. There's always a lot of people around and I like being to myself sometimes and reading or listening to my music. There are people who've used drugs, sell drugs, and even a couple of ladies who sleep with men for money around. It's odd because I thought kids like me are supposed to be protected from people like that. I could have lived a similar life with Mama.

I like the fact that my foster mother has friends of many kinds but as a child I don't understand a lot. Unlike the last home, I'm not supplied most things that I'd had and I'm not used to shopping for myself. Since the age of 15 I've used my own money. They get money every month from Social Security and it goes into a bank account. When I need something I request my money and I budget the best I can.

The first Christmas here was surprising because I had been used to having presents under a tree for me. That has stopped. I've had to grow up quick and it's scary but I don't mind because I have to do what I must to survive. At least I'm not getting beat or felt on. Danny protects me but even he gets on my nerves so much because I'm not used to anyone caring so much. One day he'll be gone.

Even though Danny crowds my space and is very protective I'm thankful for him because he keeps my hair done, we do fun things on the weekends and some weekends we just get a hotel room to spend time together and he makes holidays special with clothes and jewelry. Everyone loves my fresh Gucci link chain and I have gold on every finger. He tells me I'm worth all that and then some, says he loves me and shows me because he takes good care of me but what's love? He treats me better than I've seen any woman treated. He's different and sometimes I pinch myself to wakeup but he's real. Danny is too good to be true and I wonder what I ever did to deserve him.

Chapter 45

Sad news ripples through my ears and to my heart. Jewel has passed away and I never got to say goodbye. My cousin knows I love her and I prayed for her every night. I'm beginning to hate life. Dark clouds are setting in because as much as I can't wait to get 18 my future is a big question mark.

I tried to apply to colleges and I wanted my foster mother to go visit some with me, but she acts as if she's not interested because Tasha accused her of paying too much attention to me. I'm also accused of trying to be a goody two shoes because I'm striving to do better. When I got in trouble all the time I was ridiculed, I pick myself up and there's something wrong with that too.

I don't know about a goody two shoes but I know God has a better life for me so yes, I keep my head high and I talk smack. My mouth gets me in a lot of trouble but it's better than punching or stomping someone. Either way, they're going to have to get over it. Either they're going to get the fighter by way of my hands or my mouth but my mouth is safe and I don't want to get sent to juvenile detention.

"Janera are we going to your cousin's funeral?" Danny asks with sincerity as he devours a meal of jerk chicken, peas and rice, cabbage and plantain. He's put me onto Caribbean food and I've learned his maternal family is from Barbados. Danny teaches me a lot that and tells me it's good to explore other things than what we're used to.

As I pick at my food because I haven't had much of appetite I shake my head.

"Nope, my Aunt forbid me. I don't want any trouble. I want my cousin to have peace."

"Well how about this. You go to the wake and view her body."

"The family will see me. I said I want peace."

"You and your cousin were tight and I want you to pay your respect."

"Respect is in my heart and that's where Joyce will always remain."

It's almost time for the funeral homes closing and Danny and I constructed the perfect plan for me to see Jewel for the last time.

Getting the date, time and location from the newspaper, my boyfriend, my bodyguard, my Clyde, my everything, is driving me to Gilmore Funeral Home. My nerves are shot and I've been crying all day.

We both get out the car as the sun has set and I walk slowly to the building located on Roanoke Ave. in Newport News. The door is opened and just as Danny had said, no one is there. I'm alone and I can see my cousin's body lying in the casket. Danny is walking behind me and has found a chair to sit in as I walk to get a closer look. My face is getting hot as I feel that I'm going to explode, faint and fly away. Piercing cries and screams explode from my vocal chords, through my larynx and out my mouth. Jewel does not look like herself but she's in my heart.

Right now I can do one of two things; run or die. Run is the better option so as the track star I've never been I run as if my life depends on it and Danny isn't far. My soul is worn, my mind jumbled and heart is deflated. Like a baby I'm snotting and drooling. The heat of my body feels better in the cool air as my mind travels and goes blank.

Not remembering much but a few words I don't know how I've made it back into the house. Shielding my face still filled with flowing tears I run upstairs and go to the bathroom to shower and get ready for bed as death fills my every thought.

Chapter 46

Sinking back into how I used to be, I want to press the button to the right to fast forward to November 4, 1993. I'm gonna snatch those walking papers and tell social services to kiss my ass. I'm angry that my biological mother now makes no effort to see me and I'm mad that Daddy died and now my cousin is dead.

At this point my only option is to run far away from here. An argument with my foster mother has sent me there. My mouth has gotten my in trouble and she's chosen to jack me up in a corner in my room. Instead of fighting back physically I have chosen to run. Sometimes I think people expect me to react a certain way and I walk into traps. I've learned to control myself a great deal, but today is not one of those days I want to use it.

Losing grip on life I'm out of the house wearing a peasant looking sweater with a flower skirts, and some clogs. My attire is not weather appropriate but I don't care. My destination is unknown so I find myself at a bus stop. At least I can pretend to be going somewhere. Most people don't know where they're going anyway and I'm blending in. Most people are clueless anyway, shouldn't make decisions and have damn sure made crazy decisions for me. Mama isn't the only crazy one. They fit right in with her. Grandma says that the pot calls the kettle black and everyone is black because everyone is messed up, but want to point a finger.

Just like that, I'm forced to go to another home. I kinda thought I'd never leave the home I've been in for the past two years but everything comes to an end.

Danny is with me every step of the way and some people don't understand our relationship.

Life is passing me by and I don't care about anything. Danny is now beginning to be my least favorite person because he got locked up for a little bit. He disappointed me because he taught me to be smart. He got caught and supposedly sold drugs to an undercover. I walked past the jail a few times but never went to see him because I didn't want to see my guy in jail.

Now that he's out he thinks things will be the same but they're not. He's now showed me that he's weak. Showing me how to look at everything, scan scenes watching for police of 5-0 he slipped. He's now one of them and I want to explore my options and see other guys.

I've been sent to yet another home and almost got in a fight with one of my foster sisters. Danny saved her from a serious butt whipping.

"Girl, who you think you talking to? I told you to leave me alone but you keep pushing my buttons. You don't want none of this. I hate you." Danny knew that this girl irritates me to no end so he rushed to the home knowing that my new foster mother is at work.

"You not going to do anything to me." Shanda, my irritating foster sister is now following me as I walk to my room.

"Little girl, I told you to leave me alone. I'm trying to cool off and keep from whipping your ass." Just like that I've slapped the taste from her mouth and Danny rushes down the hall to grab me.

"Get the fuck off of me. I hate all of y'all. Nobody really knows or loves me." Trying to break free from his hold I almost forgot how big this dude is but I give up and lay limp as I strategize and count to three silently.

At three I turn into the Incredible Hulk and use the strength from my lower body to wrap around his tightly, as I bite his shoulder and try to claw his eyes out. Knowing he'd lose his grip, I jump up and slide my right hand under the mattress retrieving my knife I'd hidden. People never knew that I started a habit of hiding knives just in case and this is when I need it.

Neither Danny nor Shanda can see the blade because I know how to hide weapons, learned it from Mama. With the knife up my sleeve I see Danny trying to approach me again.

"Didn't I say leave me the hell alone. Break up with me. Let me live my life. Nobody loves me and I want you out of my life. Find somebody else. Why you want to love a foster kid anyway?"

As he reaches for me I flick the blade from my sleeve and as quick and as smooth as Zorro, my first love is bleeding. Shanda is screaming and dialing 911 and all that I know is to run.

Chapter 47

That Danny must be crazy because he fled the scene which saved me big time. There's no victim so there's no charges. The police and social services came to the scene and I was still in a rage. The ladylike crap is out the door and I feel like a caged animal wanting to be free.

My refuge is Alicia. She's been my partner in crime for a little over a couple years, she doesn't run her mouth and I trust her. With Danny I'm Bonnie and with Alicia I'm Louise of Thelma and Louise. Alicia's always there for me and I get her caught up in the craziest situations like the time I call myself hanging out with an ex. Danny was chasing us all through the town starting on Pembroke Ave. Alicia was a little shook because she knows my guy is insane at times but together we laughed for days. There was also the time where we suspected her guy of cheating. I somehow masterminded a plan to get him to open the hotel room door where he was with another female. He fell into my trap but only enough to open the door to peer his head out and catch a jab to the jaw by me.

Right now Alicia is the closest thing to family and she looks out for me so looking out for her is a must. Her family even looks out for me because they allow me to stay with them here and there. They know that I'm a foster kid and that's it. Maybe my eyes show the pain which makes them care. Alicia's family will be blessed for shielding me and taking care of me in my time of need.

Not only am I on the run from the system, I'm running from Danny. The day he was released from the hospital and bandaged up with stitches he searched for me. He's been there to no end but I want out. I'm not used to anyone staying and I just want to breathe. I'm going to do bad things to him if he doesn't leave and I can feel it.

Danny was there when I was in the group home, he was there in all the homes for the past three years, and he was there when I was robbed at my part-time job. Only he and my coworkers know that a gun was put to my head as my life flashed before my eyes and I was prepared to die. That night although it was surprising to be grabbed up while cleaning up for the night at Kentucky Fried Chicken, I was ready. Just like every other time my life was spared. Second time I've had to look down a barrel of a gun. The first was with Mama and her games and then the guy who I heard was from Panama who snatched me like a doll as he told me he would kill me if he didn't get money.

Although I haven't been to church in a while I know that God and his angels are with me and I keep getting spared. Danny says I'm magical and I laugh it off. Maybe he says that because I've been into unicorns for years and I like to look at pretty crystal balls and read astrology.

My reasoning for being on the run is because I'm tired. They told me they're going to put me in a shelter but who do they think I am? A foster kid in a shelter? That would mean I'm double homeless. With Alicia by my side I'm good and always will be.

I'm at my freedom mark which is 18 and I'm going to school but not really. Physically I'm there, but everything is a blur. My mind is fuzzy and I don't want to be in school with kids my age getting ready for college when I have to worry about where I'm going to lay my head. I want to stay in school but it's hard. School and job are two things I must keep. I need an education and I gotta eat. I told Danny I want my independence. He says we should go to New York. Yeah right, I'll probably die the first week.

Asking around, I find out how to get emancipated. At first, I thought they'd just let me go because I'm 18 but no. They say I have to petition the court. At the age of 18,

I am legally an adult but I have to ask permission to live my own life. Dumb ass rules, but I will play them as I have the past 15 years. Like a game of jump rope they make a move and then I jump in and hope I don't get tangled or fall.

My social worker with the penniless loafers is no longer with the agency. They probably shipped his nonworking, no penny having, bifocal wearing ass somewhere else. Maybe they're retraining him because God knows he missed a lot of the hints I threw his way.

Under my old social workers nose, I was sexually, physically and emotionally abused, my grades when up and down. I called him at night when I was ganged up on and he tattled to my foster parent who is the problem. He's a joke for real. He just showed up for his check.

My new social worker looks to be my age and I'm actually taller than her. She recently graduated from

Norfolk State and she's into fashion. Originally she's from
up north. See, I gotta research people the way they
research me. Don't think you're going to read through my
life's story and give me nothing. Child, please. She has
info on me and I have info on her. I even know her sons
name and he's a cutie.

As much as I want to be nice and sweet I can't
because I have to protect myself and she seems like she's
doing her job but it's too late. No Pennies messed it up for
all social workers. They didn't protect me the past seven
years and now I'm done. I want to break up with Danny
and Social Services.

Danny has taught me enough about the streets these
past years so I'm good. I know how to make money and
take care of myself and I just exist anyway. Weed is now
my relief from pain; my medicine and I take it every day. I
don't have to buy it because I roll with the weed man and

we're tight. He listens to me and we smoke, eat and laugh

nonstop.

Just like that I'm nonstop at the courthouse and it's

my court date.

"Young lady, please tell the court why you want the

Hampton Department of Social Services released as your

guardian." The judge looked at me as if the spotlight is

now mine.

"Your honor, I feel that it be in the best interest of

the court to release me from the custody of the Hampton

Department of Social Services because they are unable to

provide adequate care." Keeping my head high I watch as

Judge Dee scribbles something on paper. The system

taught me a lot too. Now knowing how to use their words I

threw them back. Now take that to the bank.

In the blink of an eye I'm free. Thank the Lord,

praise God I'm free. Now I have to dodge Danny and go

hit up the mall. I'm free. This is my happily ever after and one day I'll have my Dad's last name to show him I acknowledge his fight. I'm a fighter too.

About the Author

Karm Banks is a true artist and takes great pride in raising four children of her own as well as caring for many others. She has a passion for giving back and promoting literacy by way of Literally Speaking Book and Social Club in which she founded in 2009.

Karma loves spending time with loved ones, listening to music, designing clothes and gardening. She feels that God gave us all we need but it's up to us to utilize life's tools.

Karma will forever be a voice for many who are shackled by silence. She knows that together as we share our stories we will not only find that we are not alone but we are also able to heal.

Want to contact Karma?

Email: karma@iamkarmabanks.com

Website: www.iamkarmabanks.com

Facebook: www.facebook.com/iamkarmabanks

Instagram & Twitter: @iamkarmabanks

Made in the USA
Charleston, SC
27 April 2016